KU-333-982

THE SHINING HIGHWAY

AN ACCOUNT OF A
PLAIN MAN'S PILGRIMAGE

THE SHINING HIGHWAY

AN ACCOUNT OF A
PLAIN MAN'S PILGRIMAGE

BY

H. L. GEE

THE EPWORTH PRESS
(EDGAR C. BARTON)
25-35 CITY ROAD, LONDON, E.C.1

All rights reserved
First published, June 1935
Second impression, January 1936
Third impression, October 1937
Fourth impression, October 1938
Fifth impression, April 1939
Sixth impression, February 1940
Seventh impression, November 1940
Eighth impression, June 1941

Made in Great Britain

To
ALL PILGRIMS

CONTENTS

I climb a hill and think about the high places of
the earth; talk with a gentleman of the road; am
informed that one should never miss 'a hopportunity'; help a charming motorist in distress; travel
by car (almost) against my will; talk with a
doomed man; and set out on a wild-goose chase.

I walk in the dark; explore a lonely, unfamiliar
world; watch the dawn; have breakfast in a little
gold mine; hear the involved story of a man with a
handcart; ride in company with a remarkable 'bus
conductor; am caught in a shower; and walk the
last half mile with a shining host.

Thanks are due to the Editors of the following periodicals for permission to reproduce portions of some of my contributions: *The Bedford Record, The Children's Newspaper, The Cornish Guardian, The Dundee Evening Telegraph, The Goole Times* Series, *The Halifax Courier, The Harrogate Herald* Series, *The Huddersfield Examiner, The Leamington Morning News, The Manitoba Free Press, The Mansfield Chronicle, The Newcastle Evening Chronicle, The Northamptonshire Evening Telegraph, The Scarborough Mercury* Series, *The Stirling Observer, The Streatham News* Series, *The Watford Observer, The Whitby Gazette*, and others.

Without a parable spake He not

CHAPTER I

*I begin a walking tour by riding fifty miles in a car; talk with a
young optimist in blue slippers; sleep in a meadow; advise a
disgruntled young man; make the acquaintance of the landlord of
The Three Wise Men; and hear an odd story about a locked
cupboard.*

I SET OUT with the intention of walking all the
way, or most of it, or at any rate part of it. I
thought of myself as a pilgrim, and if I had any
vow to fulfil it was to talk to any one who would
listen, and to listen to any one who would talk. My
friends urged me to stay at home. I thanked them
for their good counsel, and began my pilgrimage
a little before eight one summer morning.

As I closed the creaking gate I felt the thrill of a
new way of life. Like Alexander, I had a world
to conquer, though I intended invading only a
small part of it. Columbus had no brighter dreams
than I, nor was Christian more blithe when he
beheld a shining light afar off. I thought of my
cautious friends who were probably in bed even
at that hour, and was glad I had followed the
devices of my own heart.

Let me be honest and confess that a motoring
friend had promised to take me the first fifty miles
of my walking tour. I had hardly reached the
cross-roads when he drove up, his punctual arrival
reminding me of the chariot of fire which appeared

for Elijah when his time was come, though I took care not to mention this thought to him lest he should take it as a reflection on the age of his car. After I had thrown my haversack in the rear and had taken my seat, my friend remarked, 'You are setting off in glorious weather. I almost wish I were coming all the way with you.'

'We should get along without quarrelling, no doubt,' I said, 'but it wouldn't do. To begin with, Stevenson and Hazlitt are of the opinion that a walking tour should be gone upon alone.'

'A *walking* tour? Of course, of course. It hardly looks like one so far, does it?'

'Appearances are often deceptive,' I reminded him. 'For example, any one would take you for a shrewd business man.'

'I gather that you think I'm not?'

'Can you wonder? Is it a month since you were discussing a plan for giving money away? Surely that is not good business? Besides, are you not giving me a lift in your car for which I presume there is no charge? Of course, I know you *are* a good business man, but you are something more, so much more than I, who have known you twenty years, do not know all there is to know about you. Are you not, indeed, one of the millions of universes we call men and women, all bundles of surprises, and every bundle worth unpacking? That is partly why I am going on this *walking* tour.' (I stressed the last word but one.)

'I dare say you are right,' he admitted, adding, 'you will find some queer folk before the journey is done.'

After driving through a pleasant countryside we climbed the hills and came to a broad plain. The road ran among woods and villages, over little bridges, and by gardens and orchards and farms. There were churches shaded by trees, and old mansions in parks where knights and ladies had walked in what is said to have been Merrie England. A castle, long in ruins, linked the summer morning with the grim days of the barons. A turn in the road gave us a peep of the grey walls of a monastery by a river. We were in an England where pious monk and daring knight, lord and squire, servitor and pilgrim had had their day and ceased to be. Though the memory of them was dear to me it was not the ghosts of the past but the men and women of the present I had come to see.

A few more miles brought us to the place where we had agreed to part; he, as he insisted on reminding me, to go on to do an honest day's work, I to begin my pilgrimage in earnest. Wishing me God-speed, he drove off, leaving me to follow a country road, knowing it was bound to bring me somewhere if I kept on long enough.

I wore old clothes and old shoes. My few possessions were in a haversack, and I carried a little money that I might be able to pay my reckoning. Before leaving home I had looked round my shelves, and had chosen two small volumes, *Virginibus Puerisque* which I had stuffed into one pocket of my jacket, and the *Imitation of Christ*, which had gone into the other. Thomas à Kempis did well to write the *Imitation of Christ*, one of the most comforting and inspiring books I know; but Stevenson, I think, should have known better than to give some of his most charming essays the intimidating title of *Virginibus Puerisque*. If any schoolboy with his dreams, or any young man contemplating marriage, or any married man contemplating suicide has handled this book without reading it, why, the author has no one but himself to blame. But it is worth opening, for it has a wealth of good humour and manly courage and sound common sense; and among other things are shrewd observations on walking tours. He says:

'To be properly enjoyed, a walking tour should be gone upon alone. If you go in company, or even in pairs, it is no longer a walking tour in anything but name. A walking tour should be gone upon alone because freedom is of the essence; because you should be able to stop and go on, and follow this way or that as the freak takes you; and because you should have your own pace, and neither trot alongside a champion walker, nor mince in time with a girl. And then you must be open to all impressions, and let your thoughts take colour from what you see. *You should be as a pipe for any wind to play upon.*'

There you have the whole matter in a nutshell. So much of our time to-day is spent in doing something or going somewhere, or keeping appointments, or worshipping clocks, that some of us lose the art of being receptive. We hurry along the road at breakneck speed without seeing half the colours and the shapes of things, without hearing the music in familiar voices or wondering at the mystery of the common day. To go upon a walking tour alone, therefore, to travel without doing homage to any tyrannical objective; for once in a lifetime to be passive rather than active,—this is to be a pipe for any wind to play upon.

Mile after mile I walked, the glory of the morning tingling in my veins. A lark sang overhead, and every turn of the road brought me to new beauty. Nevertheless, I began to wonder how long it would be before I fell in with some adventure. I was still wondering when I walked into one.

I had caught sight of a distant town and had thought of breaking my fast there when I heard someone singing:

> 'When I was a lad I served a term
> As office-boy to an attorney's firm,
> I cleaned the windows and I swept the floor,
>   And I polished up the handle of the big front door.
>   I polished up the handle so carefulee
>   That now I am the Ruler of the Queen's Navee.'

Crossing the road I looked over a garden wall and saw a young man on his knees. I waited till the verse was finished before saying, 'Good morning. I love Gilbert and Sullivan. May we have another verse?'

The young man sprang nimbly to his feet. 'Hello?' he said. 'I didn't know there was an audience. Glad to see you. Great stuff, Gilbert and Sullivan.'

Bн

'I never grow tired of it,' I said.

'Oh, I grow tired of it, but it comes in handy for a change. Marjorie is so amazing that she actually hums Delius! She sends the baby to sleep with Stravinski, poor child.' He was laughing as he spoke. He had long hair, small hands, a merry, boyish face, and bright little eyes, and he seemed to be bubbling over with good humour and friendliness and satisfaction. He wore a red and yellow pull-over and a white cricket shirt open at the neck, and his feet were pushed into blue slippers. He held a pair of shears before him, the points near his nose.

'You look as if you have been working hard,' I said.

He nodded. 'Very,' he declared. 'I've been at it since six o'clock this morning—ten minutes off for breakfast. I didn't intend spending so much precious time on the lawns, but the mower ran away with me, and I felt that once having put my hand to the plough—you know the rest. However, as Quintilian says, "everything that has a beginning comes to an end." A solemn thought for a summer morning.'

'Well, anyhow,' I said, thinking of moving on, 'hard work does not spoil your good spirits. You seem very happy.'

He cut the air with his shears. 'That is precisely where you are wrong,' said he. 'I do not merely *seem* happy. I *am* happy.'

'Nobly spoken,' I replied. 'It is a delight to find someone for whom life goes easily, and to whom living . . .'

'Ah,' said he, 'but you are mistaken again. Life doesn't go easily for me, thank heaven.'

The last two words banished all my thoughts of moving on. I leaned over the gate, and looked at him in surprise. 'My dear man,' I said, 'you astonish me. Kindly explain the meaning of that last remark.'

He threw the shears on a heap of grass, interlocked his fingers, and stood on his toes. 'Why,' said he gaily, 'there's nothing to explain. I merely said life was not easy. And I am thankful. You know how Cicero observes that great men rejoice in adversity as brave soldiers triumph in war. Only I'm not great, of course.'

'Isn't it rather unusual to look at things that way?'

'Is it? Well, it shouldn't be. But people say we are a queer trio.'

'You are married then?'

'To the most charming, wonderful, sensible, delightful girl in the world. It was awfully good of her to have me when there was little else.'

'How do you mean?'

'Well, I'm not much to begin with, and when we were married three years ago we had only just enough money to build this house, and furnish two rooms, though we had a soap-saver and a pan in the scullery.' His bright little eyes were laughing—whether at me or himself I could not be sure.

'So that was how you began married life?'

'That was it. The lawn-mower,' he glanced at the machine on the path, 'is our latest acquisition.

It arrived on Saturday—that is really why I've been using it to-day. Childish of me, of course. When we settled down here our friends and relatives came to look at us—and their wedding presents, mostly fish knives, and Marjorie and I don't eat fish, and Michael can't. The butter dishes came in handy—we broke three in the first month; but then, Seneca says, "the worst gives us a chance to do our best." And life is short, of course, butter or no butter. We had a beautiful pair of vases, but no sideboard to put them on.'

'Dear me.'

'Oh, don't say, "Dear me," like that. That was the glory of it! That was the thrill!'

'Not having a sideboard?'

'Naturally. You know Browning? You'll remember what he says about the Greek statues?'

'Yes, I know. But forgive me if I don't quite see the connexion between Greek statues and not having a sideboard.'

He ran his fingers through his hair. 'Well,' he explained impatiently, 'it's the same idea, of course. You see, the trouble with the Greek statues was that they were perfect. Think of the horror of being perfect—beyond all hope of improvement. Finished! Complete! At the end . . . horrible!' He shuddered. 'I'm not perfect—neither is Marjorie, though she's an angel. So, you see, we can improve. Life's not finished, not rounded off. Neither is the house.'

'Yes, but the sideboard?'

'Oh, well, I'm coming to that. You see, we

were poor, and still are; well, that meant we came
into a house only one-third furnished. Well, that
meant that day by day and week by week we had
the joy of furnishing it, seeing it grow nearer and
nearer completion and perfection. So it has gone
on. I paid for a black bowl for the lounge last
week, and now the lounge is finished according to
schedule. Glorious!'

'But wouldn't it have been wiser to have put
off your marriage a year or two?'

'Sir, you amaze me! You look intelligent and
are not! Put if off? For what? Wait? How long?
For old age and wisdom? For money enough to
buy a palace *en bloc*, and never have the fun of
buying it bit by bit? She loved me—a miracle, I
grant you. I loved her. All the old fossils said,
wait, wait, wait. We laughed at them. We put
our money in a heap, and a precious little one it
was. We made a beginning. Once having made
a beginning you can go on, as Ausonius has it in
his epigrams, "To begin is half the work!" So we
began. Then we went on. Marvellous! Marjorie
taught music and elocution in the town—she's
L.R.A.M., you know, and turned *arpeggios* into a
carpet. You ought to come and see it in the bedroom. The poultry helped, of course.'

'You mean the money she earned?'

'Of course, of course! Music and carpets,
elocution and a hammock, poultry and a new
dinner service. I gave three lectures and bought
the sideboard. We live in thoughts not years! I
was in the teaching profession—Latin, Greek, and
handwriting for the younger boys. I turned finite

verbs and Latin syntax into a wardrobe and a set of Galsworthy—I mean I wrote a new Latin primer. It sells well in the schools. I brought out another three weeks after we got back from our honeymoon. We went to Grange-over-Sands and took illustrated guides of Venice and Rome. Rome! Ah, I hadn't thought of it till now, Rome was not built in a day! It is an inspiration I must use in my next bit of writing. Yes, I write for one or two periodicals, and have set up as an art critic, though I don't know the first thing about art. But the editors think I do. It's wonderful what a difference a neatly typed manuscript makes. I've run a series of articles on Italy in England. It's mostly Marjorie's idea, and we've turned it into one quarter of a rocking-horse for Michael.'

'Magic,' said I.

'You're right. Well then, I've translated a couple of books, and made something out of them. They helped to pay for the furnishing of the spare bedroom, though we don't want too many visitors. That's why we chose this house which everyone says is dumped down far from anywhere. Peace, quiet, seclusion, these are the foundations of inspiration. I must not forget Rome. I made my bookcase out of coaching a fellow who gave me Balzac when he got through.'

'But isn't all this hard work?'

'Of course.'

I looked at him. 'And you do not object to hard work?'

'Object? Why should I?'

'I don't know. I didn't think you would. But

what about playing golf or whist?' (I smiled as I spoke.)

'Excellent games,' he replied. 'Marjorie and I play golf and whist every spare minute of the day —and night, only,' and here his bright little eyes danced, 'we never have any spare minutes, thank heaven. We are trying to make our fortunes. The birds build their nests stick by stick—and Rome was not built in a day. I must not forget that. But come and see Marjorie and Michael. I do not know who you are, but it doesn't matter. Come along.' He was hurrying up the path as he spoke. 'Marjorie! Here's a gentleman with a depraved taste in music. He likes Gilbert and Sullivan. Forgive him, my dear. Where are you? Woman, advance!'

The 'woman' advanced, a charming girl with dark hair escaping from a most fetching red dust-cap. It did not seem to occur to her to ask who I was. She took me as I was, and showed me round the house, her husband hovering round, and push-ing in a word or two here and there, sometimes in English, often in Latin. Proud indeed they were of their house, and with much laughter and many sly remarks they showed me the lounge which had been so oddly furnished, and told me stories of how the clock had been bought by a recital of modern American verse, the cut-glass vase bought to celebrate the publication of the cheap edition of the primer. I was privileged to look into the author's den, a most amazing little room with books and papers on every chair, and some under the table. Marjorie whisked out of the room 'to see to a cauliflower' as she said, and while she was gone the author showed me first one book, and then another. Here was a slim volume bought with the money he had intended for a tie; here a set of Anatole France given him when he left his last school. Here were recent volumes sent to him for review, and inside were the reviews he had written, some scathing indeed. There were Roman and Greek authors, and a little group of Spanish master-pieces, 'bound in Morocco' as he remarked.

Then Marjorie appeared and bustled us into the garden where I had to be introduced to Michael who lay crowing in his pram.

When I meet a lion, I shoot it. When I find a spider in the bathroom I attack it with a sweeping brush. When a burglar breaks into my house I telephone for the police. In all these circum-stances I know what to do, and do it. But when a baby looks at me with—may I say?—sardonic eyes, eyes with a gentle, smiling contempt mingled with infinite pity, I feel I am a nincompoop. I say something which immediately sounds unwarrant-ably Aristotelian. I say something else and blush because when I have put it into pretty baby prattle to which the little one disdains to reply, I feel he has won again. All this is discon-certing.

Apparently these two astonishing people had a secret signal, for while I was admiring the baby, Marjorie brought three cups of coffee and a walnut cake, all on a breadboard. 'We haven't a silver tray, *yet*,' she explained. 'We shall have one some day. Meanwhile, you must try my cake. It is home-made, and if you do not say it is the most delicious cake you have ever tasted . . .'

'You will be a brave and honest man,' put in her husband.

We talked there in the garden, and I marvelled at the outlook on life these two had. They were practical idealists who seemed to be making a fine thing of life. It was hard work to drag myself from them, but at last I made my bow to Michael, gave Marjorie my sympathy (with reference to her husband, as I was careful to explain), received her expression of thanks, and was accompanied to the garden gate by the amateur gardener who thanked me for calling, demanded a promise that I would never pass that way again without calling to see them, and remarked that life was a great adventure, quoting Horace to prove that we are all made up of inconsistencies. He stood on the gate to call out 'Excelsior!' after I had taken to the road.

That my first adventure should have been so exhilarating I regarded as a good omen; and as I plodded on to the town I wondered if in all my pilgrimage I could hope to find more wonderful people than these three adventurers.

Now, as I said, I had intended breaking my fast in the town, but as the coffee and cake had taken the edge off my appetite I determined to keep right on (as Milton says), till I found a pleasant spot to lie down. So I went through the little town with its solemn houses, and closed doors, it shops where few people were buying or selling, and its school where the children were singing, and its church with a spire pointing men to higher things, and a clock which chimed half past one at twenty-eight minutes to two. A mile or so along a road between high hedges brought me to a gate which I climbed without asking leave of any one, and having thrown my burden to the ground (Christian's burden fell of its own accord, you remember), I stretched myself on a living carpet, and after a brief meditation on the wisdom of daring and the glory of conquering, I fell asleep.

I awoke some hours afterwards, stiff and thankful, stiff with walking farther than usual, and thankful that England, which has lost so many good things in the last century, has kept her meadows. Presently I struggled to my feet, climbed the gate without asking leave of any one, and resumed my journey.

I had not gone far when I fell in with a young fellow who was trying to pump up a bicycle tyre. Glancing up, red in the face, he looked anything but pleasant. 'A puncture?' I asked. (With such commonplace remarks will even wise men address their fellows.)

'I should jolly well think so,' he grumbled. 'It's the second this week.'

'Dear me,' I said.

He shut the pump with a snap, and kicked the flat tyre petulantly. 'It's that idiot's confounded carelessness,' he muttered. 'I knew if I lent it him again he'd ruin it. About time he bought a bike of his own. There's nothing for it but walking home.'

'Shall we go along together?'

'Oh, just as you please.' He took the handlebars, and began pushing the cycle. 'They'll be wondering where I am,' he said, looking at the long stretch of road before us. 'And the road,' he added angrily, 'is enough to drive a fellow mad.'

'The road?'

'I'm sick of it.'

'What is the matter with it?'

'Everything. You'd jolly well know if you had to cycle along it twice every day of your life.'

'Seven days a week?'

'No, six days a week. It's enough, isn't it?'

'I couldn't say.'

'I say it is! I ought to know. I've cycled along this road every day—six days a week—for over five years. I know every inch of it. I cycle to my work and back day after day.'

'Walking will be a pleasant change, then?'

'Trying to be funny?'

I shook my head. I was thinking of the difference between this young man and the one I had met earlier in the day; but I was interested in him, and though I do not usually talk at great length, I began to speak to him for the good of his soul. 'I think this one of the most delightful roads in England,' I said. 'There are trees and hedges. There are flowers prasing God with sweetest looks. Amid these pleasant things perhaps you will allow me to introduce you to a wise man of long ago. I carry his words of wisdom in my pocket—and some in my heart, and this man was Thomas à Kempis whose earnest thoughts I often meditate upon.' Here, having found a familiar page, I read

aloud: 'A good man turneth all things to good.'
Then I went on to say, 'And Epictetus, I believe,
observed also that there is nothing good or ill save
in the will. It would appear, then, that the world
is what we take it to be. You follow?'

'No, I'm blessed if I do.'

'Blessed, indeed, are you,' said I, 'if you understand. I tell you, a prophet speaketh, saying,
to-morrow when you come this way you shall love
this road . . .'

'Perhaps!'

'Certainly. You shall see new wonder and
beauty in it, and shall thank God for it because it
will take you to your work, the best place any
road can take any man—with one exception.'

He looked up quickly. 'What's that?' he asked.

'Home again when the work is done,' I said.

I paused, half expecting a contemptuous reply,
but he was silent.

'And let us consider,' I said (conscious, as I
spoke, that I was being rather overbearing), 'that
some men have a home and no work. They need
our sympathy. Some have neither home nor work,
may Providence keep them from harm and from
themselves. But you have been working for over
five years. You have your work to ride to every
morning, and your home to ride back to every
evening—a place where kindness awaits you.'

'How do you know?'

'Are you not anxious to arrive? And then, again,
you are a good fellow . . .'

'Oh? I'd like to know what makes you think
that.'

'Didn't you lend your cycle to a friend?'

'Well?'

'Not only once, but twice? I found you at your worst. I rather liked you at your worst. What a delightful fellow you must be at your best!'

He smiled reluctantly.

Then I opened Thomas à Kempis again, and read once more his words about a good man turning all things to good, and I said that it was true, and that the fortune and misfortune we found were both capable of enriching our lives.

By this time we were come to a parting of the ways. I began to think I had talked too much, so I asked him to forgive me for setting myself up as his mentor, and with a rather abrupt, 'Good day,' I turned up the side-road.

But he called after me. 'Excuse me,' he said. 'I'm the one who needs forgiving. I reckon I was stupid to make so much of such a little thing—but it *was* annoying. Anyhow, I think I see what you mean. I won't forget, and perhaps it is a good thing I had a puncture!'

Then I went back and shook hands with him, saying nothing. So he went his way and I mine, and because any fool can give advice, I was still uncertain as to whether I had been wise to talk to him as I had done.

I should think the time was about six o'clock. There were still some hours of daylight left, but my thoughts turned to supper and a bed for the night. A thrush on a gatepost tried to recapture what Browning calls the first fine careless rapture he had known earlier in the year. A little wind stirred in the highest branches of the elms standing like sentinels by the road. I looked over cornfields and pastures to a wooded hill, a background for a few houses and a church, and it was only when I saw them that I realized I was tired.

I did not complain about feeling tired, first because there was no one to complain to; and second, because a man *should* be tired at the end of the day. I passed a field where one or two haymakers were at work. I saw a lad bring four horses to a pond and stand by them as they drank. There were white cottages, gardens with lupins like little spires, a spacious green, and a gabled inn with high roofs and many windows, and a large corner stone with an inscription which said, 'Asses may lean against me.' As I came up to the inn a man appeared at the doorway, a tall man in shirt-sleeves, his honest face very good to see. He was smoking a pipe, and above his head was a sign with the words, *The Three Wise Men*.

'Good evening,' said I to the landlord, for such I rightly took him to be. 'Have you food for a hungry man?'

'If he will eat it,' was the reply.

'And something to drink?'

'If he will drink it.'

'And a bed for a weary traveller?'

'If he will lie in it.'

'Then,' said I, 'thus far come I and no farther, for I will stay at the house of an honest man.'

He smiled and bade me follow him indoors where I was introduced to his wife who showed me to a low, clean bedroom, and left me to plunge my hot hands and face into cold water. Some of my weariness fell from me, and I felt the simple act of cleansing to be a sacrament, a holy ceremony of purification, a baptism into new life.

My host met me at the foot of the stairs and led me with a quaint courtesy to the parlour, a large, oak-panelled room with five windows facing south and west, their little panes golden in the light of the sun. There were diamonds of light on the sanded floor, and a bright beam across the face of the grandfather clock, the single hand of which pointed to one; I could have thought that Time stood still in that room.

After a little exchange of courtesies I said, 'The name of this inn pleases me. I am curious to know why it is called *The Three Wise Men*.'

'Why,' said the landlord, closing an eye as he spoke, 'all I can tell you is that the name was given by my great-grandfather when he settled here. How he came to choose the name I do not know, but I know he was an odd fellow in many ways, and that he did many strange and unaccountable things.'

'The stone for asses?'

He nodded. 'Yes, that was one of his pranks. If there was one thing he hated more than another it was to see an idle fellow.'

'But *The Three Wise Men*?'

'They are living now, sir, and the first is a bachelor because he is not married; the second— so my great-grandfather used to say—is a poor man because he has few cares.'

'And the third?'

The landlord took his pipe from his mouth and bowed. 'Yourself, sir, because you are not outside this inn.' His blue eyes were smiling at me. 'And speaking of wisdom,' he added, 'even simpletons can be wise now and then, for you will remember the story of the fool and the miller?'

I said I did not.

'Why, there was a miller who thought much of himself, and there was a poor simpleton who thought nothing, and these two met in the market-square one day, and the miller planned to trip the simpleton. Said he, "Come here, fool, and let us try your wit. Answer me and say if there be one thing you know."

'Then the simpleton considered well before he replied, "Aye, I know one thing. I know a miller's pigs are always fat."

' "Oh ho," cried the miller. "You know that, eh? Then tell me what you do *not* know!" and he winked to the company as he spoke.

'So the simpleton knuckled his forehead, saying slowly, "I know a miller's pigs are always fat, but I don't know whose corn he feeds 'em on!" '

Now, when he had told this tale, he left me a little to attend to customers, but returning presently he said, 'As you seem interested in the sign outside I might tell you something more about my great-grandfather. It is rather a strange story—but perhaps you are too tired to hear it?'

I assured him I was anxious to hear it.

He did not answer immediately, but stood with his half-bare arms folded across his broad chest, his eyes to the ground. At last he looked up. 'It will do to fill in five minutes while supper is being prepared,' he said. 'It is a tale I often tell to strangers—Martha calls it my sermon. Well, to begin with, my great-grandfather prided himself on being a man of his word, and it was he—as I discovered only an hour or two before my father's death—who instituted the Cupboard of Promise.'

I followed his glance to the darkest corner of the room where I saw a cupboard let into the recess between the chimney and the farther wall. 'I should like to know more about it,' I said.

'My father died when I was twenty-four. Just before he went he called me to him and begged me to swear that I would never open the door of this cupboard.' Here he raised his hand, and let his fingers rest lightly on the oak door a little above his head. 'I confess,' he said, 'this cupboard had always been a bit of a mystery, but I had never troubled my head much about it. I was surprised when my father told me to open a drawer in his dressing table and take out a little key. "That key will open the cupboard in the parlour," he told me, "but you must promise never to fit it to the lock, nor open the door."

'At first I thought him delirious, being near his end; but seeing how earnest he was, I began to ask why so strange a charge should be laid on me, to which he replied that a similar charge had been laid on him by my grandfather. Then he told me that as a family our word had always been as good as our bond; and when, to humour him,

Сн

I had sworn I would never open the cupboard, he blessed me. He died that same evening about sunset.

'Well, sir, the months went by, and a year or so later I married the sweetest woman who ever plagued a husband or made a fruit-tart—and you are soon to sample one of them. Not once, but many times, she questioned me about this cupboard; and I tell you frankly that often when my eyes fell on it I wondered what was inside, and why, having the key, I should not bring the hidden thing to light. It was a mystery I could not fathom. Nevertheless, having given my word, the door remained shut.

'There came a day almost a year after we were married when I intended driving over to Raventhorpe to buy pigs at the market. Away I went in the middle of the morning, wearing a buttonhole in my jacket, put there by no other hands than Martha's, and a happy man was I. But not for long, for suddenly I remembered a matter I ought to have seen to before setting out, so back I came in haste, and coming into the entrance I saw my wife standing at the door of this room, her hands clasped together, her face white, and her eyes turned from me. Then, looking past her, I saw the cupboard door ajar, and she, seeing that I had found her out, tried to throw her arms about my neck, but I cast her off and flung her from me. "What is this?" I cried.

' "Will," said she, "dear Will."

' "Fool!" I shouted—for in those days, sir, I had a temper to lose.

'She implored me to listen to her, but I would have none of it, and suddenly she shrank from me for I was in a white heat of anger, and I knew not what I said to her. I only know I cursed her for her folly and for betraying our trust. God knows I spoke as if all virtue were lodged in me. Then, sir, even as I spoke, her face crimsoned, her eyes blazed defiance, and without a word she turned and left the inn.

'I say she left me, sir, and the moment she was gone I despised myself. I was a proud man and would not follow her, and like a fool I stood here not knowing what to do. After a time I began to repent of what I had done, the more because I knew myself greatly to blame, more greatly than you yet know. Not only that, for when I came to myself I looked down on the table in the corner, and a little garment lay there with the needle and thread on it, and knowing it to be prepared for the child that was soon to come, I was covered with shame.

'So, leaving the house, I hurried along the road I was sure she would have taken; and as I went I considered how I should ask her forgiveness (unworthy of it though I was, as you shall hear), and how I might beg her to come back.

'With these thoughts in mind I reached Gembling Corner, and as I turned it I saw her not a dozen yards farther on. She was sittting on the seat you passed this evening, sir, her head bowed. She did not see me till I was close to her. Down on my knees I went, but even before I could ask her forgiveness, she begged for mine; and at that I was still more ashamed. "Dear heart," said I, not daring to look into her eyes, "it is I must be forgiven. My anger kindled to-day, not because I knew my honour unstained, but because, months ago, I broke my word. *I opened the 'Cupboard of Promise' last New Year's Day.*" '

Now when my host had said this he was silent, so I asked what he had found in the cupboard.

'Nothing,' said he. 'Nothing, and yet something. Day after day for weeks after my father's death I had looked at this cupboard, puzzling what might be hidden here. Bit by bit my resolve never to open it was eaten away by curiosity. I told myself my father had been delirious. I persuaded myself that he had been tricked by my grandfather. I said, "This is a hoax—and precisely the kind of practical joke my great-grandfather would delight to play." Moreover, I considered that I was of age, that the inn was mine, and that therefore I had every right to know its secrets. And again, I had an idea that some valuable might lie behind this door. Now, sir, had I found anything inside the cupboard I might have played the renegade to my conscience, fooling myself into the belief that I had broken my word for some gain or profit; but when, with a trembling hand and in secret, as if the ghosts of three dead men were watching me with accusing eyes—when, I say, I put the key to the lock and turned it and felt the door swing back, and found *nothing*, why, sir, I knew myself for the dishonest fellow I was. I wept with anger and shame.'

He paused, and then, smiling, went on. 'And now, sir, looking back over the years, I begin to see that my great-grandfather was no fool. There was a purpose behind this trick, for honesty in a man is a virtue, no doubt, but honesty without humility is a poor thing. The cupboard truly was empty, and yet, as I said before, there was something in it—a treasure of great price; and it is something to know that to-day you should take me for an honest man.'

During the latter part of this story a girl had been quietly laying the table for supper, and presently the landlord's wife came in with a wooden tray. 'I kept the supper back,' said she laughingly. 'I knew by William's voice that he was preaching his sermon. It's the only one he has.' Then she laughed into his face, and he, with his arm about her (as if all their married days were before them) assured me that the Cupboard of Promise had brought them riches indeed.

'And fruit-tarts,' said I, pointing to the table.

'And fruit-tarts,' said he solemnly, adding, 'and by the way, so far as I know we've not had a wrong word from that day to this, have we, Martha?'

'Not one,' said she.

'Tell me,' said I, 'how is it that you dare to let strangers know this secret? Is it not your intention to leave the riddle of the cupboard for those who will come after you?'

My host shook his head. 'The little one died when he was four,' he said. 'There is no one to follow after.'

Then he left me alone in the parlour with its many windows, the fading light, the clock with its single hand pointing to one, the fruit-tart, and the Cupboard of Promise, the door of which I could not then make out because of the shadows. Peace was there, and I thought: It is easier to forgive a fault in another if that fault has been our own.

So, sitting there in the twilight, my thoughts were of the landlord, an honest man, not merely in the opinions of others, but because, having been weighed and found wanting, he was ever afterwards trying to be more worthy. And surely his failure had made him a better man, more understanding of himself, more forgiving towards others! Many of us, believing ourselves righteous, grow arrogant, ungenerous, intolerant. Would to God we, too, had opened a Cupboard of Promise and found it empty, for in that moment we might have come face to face with our real selves, and so walk more humbly and more forgivingly. It may be that in this unfinished world a generous, humble sinner honestly trying to be good is to be preferred to a saint whose selfish righteousness is impeccable.

And these thoughts led me to Thomas à Kempis where he says:

'Endeavour to be patient with the defects and infirmities of others, whatsoever they be, for that thyself also hast many failings which must be borne by others. If thou canst not make thyself such a one as thou wouldst, how canst thou expect to have another in all things to thy liking? And thus it appeareth how seldom we weigh our neighbours in the same balance with ourselves.'

I smoked a pipe and thought about my host's story. Then I read another page of Thomas, and having said, 'Good night,' to everyone, I went to bed. I remember hearing the village clock strike eleven, and wondering who wound it up, and how often he did it.

CHAPTER II

I rise early and see England before breakfast; find a village blacksmith with six of one and half a dozen of another; learn a good deal about 'hosses'; am told of a mushroom tragedy; discover Capital and Labour united by a single purpose; have the company of an elfish cobbler; watch cricket played as it should be played; meet three humorists; and find a born leader of men.

I LOVE an English village. I suppose it is as far from heaven as a city, but it seems a little nearer, and early in the morning I think it is a good deal nearer. I was awake before six. My window facing south, a slanting ray of sunshine struck across the room like a spotlight from heaven; and for a little while I lay watching it move slowly down the wall. Lying there, I thought on whatsoever things are good, as St. Paul directs us, of the adventures of the day before, of the country through which I had passed, and of the people with whom I had talked. For a long time I did not think of getting up.

When I did think of it, I made haste to wash and dress, and was soon out of doors. John, who seemed to be a handy-man, was washing the entrance. He told me that he had a brother in India, that his mother was eighty-six and could thread a needle, that he did not believe in betting, and that I could go out by the back door if I had a mind to. I had. I wandered into the garden, and down to the orchard where a blackbird was piping. I vaulted a low fence, and went off across a meadow, a million million pearls sparkling about my feet. I came to a little river flashing under great chestnuts, the very friends of time; and I looked back over the meadow and to the inn with its single wisp of smoke rising from the kitchen chimney (not unlike the smoke from my host's pipe), and felt that all the fresh new world belonged to me. No lord of the manor with his park covering a thousand acres could have been richer than I, or enjoyed the scene more, and he must certainly have had something to pay for the upkeep of his estate, whereas I had nothing. So pleased was I with myself for being up early in the morning— it was not yet seven o'clock—that I thought of my friends sleeping away God's precious moments; or, if awake, probably feeling sorry for me, little knowing that I was in clover in more senses than one.

A little way upstream I walked, watching the fish darting here and there, sending little galaxies of bubbles whirling to the surface to go spinning downstream like miniature solar systems. I came to a bridge of two arches. I climbed a gate, and took the road to the village, passing a labourer who touched his cap and remarked in a friendly way, 'Grand morning, mister.'

Another man came by riding a bicycle. He nodded to me and called out, 'Fine morning,' as if he had known me all his life. Plainly the people who say the English are a taciturn nation are the ones who never rise early.

I passed an open door giving me a peep of a mother and father and three children at breakfast. I heard the clock in the church tower strike half past seven, and overtook an old man who ought to have been in bed another two hours. He was dressed in corduroy, and wore a round black hat. 'Feels like being hot,' he said, as I came level with him.

I agreed, and added, 'You are astir early!'

'Aye, aye, no doubt,' said he, 'it's us old 'uns what 'as to be up in a mornin' to see 'as how the young 'uns ain't staying in bed.'

Another few yards, and I heard the ringing of a hammer on an anvil, and in the twinkling of an eye my thoughts ran down the years to my boyhood days when my great ambition had been to be a blacksmith. A cobbled street brought me to the forge where a venerable smith was at work. I must needs be talking with him, and I soon learnt that he did a bit of farming, and that his sons had a garage, and that he, himself, had still a steady eye and could shoot a hare for dinner, though he was turned seventy. He said there were still a few horses to shoe. I watched him at his work, saw the glowing metal drawn from the furnace, marvelled to see him swing his hammer with a shower of sparks about him, and rejoiced to hear the anvil chiming. 'Yes,' said he, 'I'm at work a bit early this morning. There's a job to be done, you see. Not much money out of it, but it keeps your hand in, you know. Get out!'

The last two words were not addressed to me, though I had feared so at first. They were spoken to two little girls standing hand in hand near the door. They were dressed in little pink frocks, and it was plain they had come into the world the same day.

'Get out!' said the smith in a voice that might well have scared them.

They did not move.

'Away with you!' shouted the smith, waving his hammer at them.

They laughed.

'Do you hear, you little rascals? I'll make you run!'

'But you couldn't catch us!' said the little angels, 'cos you have roomytishum in your legs!'

'The very idea!' the smith growled. Then, turning to me, he said, 'This is what the world's coming to! No respect for age! Drat 'em!' But his eyes were twinkling, and presently he put down his hammer and said, 'Oh well, I suppose it doesn't matter how busy I am, we'll have to go. You can come as well, if you like, mister.'

Then he wiped his hands with a piece of cloth, gave each little girl a finger, and took us all to see the rabbits. 'They come every morning,' he told me as we went down the garden. 'They're Robert's children—Bessie and Joan, six of one and half a dozen of the other, and you might as well try to make an iron donkey out of a gooseberry as refuse to take 'em to see the rabbits.'

A quarter of an hour after seeing the rabbits I was sitting down to breakfast, and never had I a better relish for it. There was home-fed ham with new-laid eggs, toast, and butter, and honey, and coffee, and time enough to enjoy it all. I had the morning paper to read, and before the meal was done a black cat came among the geraniums in the window, and watched me with grave eyes as if men were very curious animals.

I had intended pushing on after breakfast, but I liked the inn, and I liked my host, and I liked everything round about, so I decided to write for an hour or two in the morning, and to look round the village later in the day. The landlord told me I ought to have a word with the village cobbler, Charlie, a good fellow who was only ninety-nine per cent. He added that the Whenby eleven were playing the home team on the village green in the evening; and though, to give him his due, he did not say anything disrespectful about Lord's, he hinted that there was nowhere like the village green for seeing cricket played as it should be played.

A word with Martha was enough to have a small table and a chair carried to the end of the garden, and there, cut off from the world by my landlord's apple-trees, I put pen to paper and recorded a few of the previous day's adventures. But only a few, for I had not been writing long when an old fellow, whom to this moment I only know as George, came across the meadow, climbed the garden fence, and stood looking at me in surprise. Having put down a basket of mushrooms, he remarked conversationally, 'Writing?'

I looked up at his smiling, whiskery, wrinkled face, red and brown, like a russet apple. 'Yes,' I said shortly, and down went my head again as my pen moved industriously over the paper.

Old George leaned against an apple-tree, crossed his legs, stuck his thumbs into his waitcoat pockets, and regarded me with mild curiosity. A rebellious spirit fermented within me, and I felt like saying, 'Go away, you old fool. Can't you see I am busy?' But I held my peace, and I trust the Recording Angel was at hand.

'Does they ever pay you for writin'?' my new found friend inquired.

'I *have* been paid for writing,' I replied. 'I sometimes write for the newspapers.'

'Queer ways of making money, ain't there?'

I nodded in agreement.

'I couldn't say 'as how I've ever done any writin' myself,' he informed me. Then, holding up his right thumb for my inspection, he observed, 'I got that there trapped in a barn door when I were twelve—so that put a stop to doing anything with a pen.'

I nodded again.

'And that weren't yesterday,' he declared, his brown face breaking into a grin. 'Nor the day before, neither. Things was a sight better when I were a lad—and I don't mind telling you.'

'I believe you.'

'There weren't no motors then, only hosses.'

'They are beautiful animals,' I said. 'They will go when you want them to.' (I half hoped he would take the hint.)

'Hosses'll come back,' he declared fervently. 'I've always said it, in spite of my old woman—and I'm right!'

'Ah,' said I.

'I don't hold with this here going about in a petrol can! It's a craze, that's all, same as crosswords. It'll pass. You mark my words, you'll see the gentry a-riding out in their carriages and pairs afore many years is gone.'

'That will be a pleasant sight,' said I, taking up my pen in a business-like way.

His eye fell on it. He leaned forward, and his voice became a whisper. 'See here, mister!' he said, 'you do a bit of writing for the papers?'

I inclined my head apologetically.

'You don't look much like a newspaper chap,' he told me candidly. 'We had one here when the institoot were opened, a little fellow with a sharp nose and them spectacles from America what look like motor-car lamps. Thought he was boss of the show, he did, but I put him in his place. I told him that he could write about that institoot till he bust, he wouldn't catch me reading it. "You can put that in your pipe and smoke it," I says to him. It don't do to let these 'ere London chaps think they are smarter than us. I told him that I'd tell him a few things about hosses if he would put it in his paper, but he took the huff and went hoff.' He had taken a step nearer. 'Now look here, mister,' he said. 'You look as if you have more sense. If I gave you something about hosses would you put it in a paper instead of writing a lot of stuff about what folk wear when they're bathing?'

'Oh, I don't write on topics of that sort,' I assured him.

'You don't? Well, instead of doing it, you write about hosses. Tell folk hosses is the thing they ought to understand. You tell 'em from me that as sure as eggs is eggs hosses is coming back, and coming into their own, and that afore long motor-cars'll be memories. You write that in that there paper, mister. It is the only salvation of this country, and mark my words, what I says I knows.'

'It is worth thinking about,' I said, 'and I promise you I will write about horses. In fact, if you care to leave me, I will begin writing about them now.'

He seemed overwhelmed by my good nature. 'I hope I haven't bothered you over-much about hosses,' he said politely. 'I do go on a bit when I gets talking about 'em. A friend of mine used to breed pigs, and talk, good lord, he used to talk about them in his sleep. Once you got him talking about pigs there was no stopping him. You just had to leave him, that was all, he wouldn't take no hint. Joe believed in hosses but he died afore his time. But look here, mister, if you write about hosses, my old woman'll one day be reading to me from the paper, and she'll come across something about 'em, and when she sees it in print that hosses is coming back, she'll believe it. She always does.' He paused. 'Aye,' he said thoughtfully, 'she'll believe anything what's in print. So would Joe. Poor Joe. I mind me and him gathering musher-rooms almost sixty years ago when we was lads. You'll see I've gathered a nice few this mornin'.'

'Yes,' I said. 'I see you have.'

'Good things is musher-rooms if they be musher-rooms, and not toadstools,' George observed.

'One toadstool among a potful, and you're none so well after it. Two, and you don't have many more troubles in this life. Poor Joe. He died after a pot of musher-rooms.'

'Indeed?'

'Aye. He died only a year come harvest. Me and him went to school together, and we had a fight as lads, and were friends ever after. I remember him eating musher-rooms, and I looked in the pot, and I said, "Joe, them's not all musher-rooms. Be careful." But he took no notice. He always was a bit pig-headed was Joe, maybe he got it from his pigs. "I gathered 'em myself,' he says, "and I'll eat 'em myself." ' His face was very solemn as he spoke, but there was mischief in his eyes. 'All the village turned out for his funeral, and we had a great tea.'

'So the mushrooms—or rather, the toadstools—killed him?'

George hitched the basket to his left arm. A smile broke across his wizened old face. 'No,' he said slowly. 'No, I can't say as 'ow they did. You see, he ate 'em when he were a lad—and it were heart disease what carried him off at the end, when he were just turned seventy. Still, he died *after* eating 'em, you know.'

I had to laugh. 'You're an old rogue!' I told him.

He chuckled. 'No,' said he, 'no, I'm bell-ringer at the church, only with sitting at the back and being deaf a bit, I don't hear all the sermon. But I don't have no naps, squire learned me better than that.'

He went off, though he must needs look round to say, 'Don't forget about them hosses, mister.' I saw him shuffle up the garden path and vanish at the back door of the inn. Then I turned again to my writing, and in order that I might keep my promise I made a few notes about old George and horses, and if this book should ever come into his hands, I have little doubt his eyes will light up if his wife should read what I have written about him and the important question of a universal return to the old form of locomotion.

So the time wagged on to lunch, which was served in the old room I loved, my host coming himself to make sure I had everything I needed.

An hour later I was strolling down the village looking out for a cobbler's shop—a cottage with a few pairs of boots and shoes in a window only one yard square. I found it, knocked at the door, and waited, hoping to see Charlie. There was no reply. I knocked again. A door of a cottage near by opened, and a woman put her head out and said, 'If it be Charlie you be wanting he's gone off.' Apparently my knuckles had helped to wake the neighbourhood, for another door opened and another woman put her head out and informed me that if it was Charlie I was wanting it was one of his 'moony' days. He had them now and again, and goodness knew where he might be found. My last informant, who was blessed with a loud voice, seemed to imagine that I was standing at the other end of the village, and her advice roused any who yet slumbered. Two more doors opened, and two

D H

more heads appeared, and I was informed by two people at once that Charlie had most probably gone down to the river.

How strangely life moves. How swiftly shadows overtake the sunshine! Whereas three minutes before I had rapped on Charlie's door I had had the street to myself, its silence unbroken, behold, many women were now at many doors, many eager voices advising and directing me; and since the last two females to appear gave it as their opinion that Charlie was to be found by the river, and one of the other women knew beyond any doubt that he had gone by the lane to Banks's Farm, there followed such a shower of words, such a downpour of deductions and conclusions and directions, that had those same words been drops of rain I must have been drowned.

Far be it from me to boast, for all is vanity in this world, but I hereby solemnly record this fact, that without one word more I turned on my heel and walked down the village street, leaving behind me a thunder-shower of feminine loquacity.

I took the first road which invited me by its shade, and walked slowly between sweet hedges, caring nothing where the road brought me. I had not gone far—that is, I had smoked not more than half a pipe—when I heard someone laughing so heartily, so naturally, and so infectiously, that there in the road I must needs begin laughing myself, though I had no idea what the joke might be. When silence settled down again I considered how good a thing it was that not only are measles and whooping cough catching, but also good humour and laughter; and thereupon I took out *Virginibus*, and opened it at 'An Apology for Idlers' where I read that a happy man or woman is a better thing to find than a five-pound note.

Now, as I turned a corner with *Virginibus* in my hand, my eyes on the page where these words were written, I heard another peal of laughter, or rather two peals of laughter, one almost a falsetto, the other a deep rumbling baritone laugh; and looking up I saw two men who deserve to find a place in a better book than this.

'Oh dear!' said one. 'If only she could have seen herself!'

'Man, man,' said the other, 'it's a merciful Providence that won't let any of us do that!'

Then there was more laughter.

So I went up to them, and I said, 'Gentlemen, it does me good to hear you.'

'It's doing me harm!' said one—Mr. Quinn, as I discovered later.

'No,' said I. 'That cannot be. Laughing does a man good.'

'Not in my case,' he replied. 'Or I should say, Mr. Washington's laughter doesn't do me any good.'

'And how is that?' I asked.

'Why,' said Mr. Washington himself, 'you see, Mr. Quinn—that's my partner's name—Mr. Quinn knows that if you laugh you grow fat, and if I laugh and grow fat it becomes harder work for him to push me in the removal van!'

'And it's hard enough as it is!' Mr. Quinn murmured. 'Hard enough I can tell you. He's always increasing his capital, and I'm the symbol of labour!'

Then I looked from one to the other. Mr. Washington was sitting in a large, clumsy, old-fashioned Bath chair, and by the look of him I guessed he weighed nearly fourteen stones. As for Mr. Quinn, tall and thin, there was something odd about his eyes, dull eyes that looked straight at you, but saw nothing.

'And the joke, gentlemen?' I asked. 'What was the joke?'

'Why,' said Mr. Quinn, 'there wasn't one really. My partner here keeps an eye on most things, and we were just coming along when a cow looked over the hedge—sort of made its *début*, you know, and Washington said, "Good afternoon, madam!" That was all. It doesn't sound much when you repeat it—it was just the sudden appearance of a head over the hedge—something like the Cheshire cat in *Alice in Wonderland*—you know.'

'And did you see it?' I asked, addressing Mr. Quinn.

He smiled. 'Oh no,' said he. 'I'm as blind as a bat!'

'That's why he's a friend of mine,' said Mr. Washington. 'If he could see me he'd drown himself.'

'There are compensations in every affliction,' said Mr. Quinn virtuously. 'I dare say if I could see old Washington here, I should think him too heavy to push in the old Bath chair.'

'Push him?' I repeated. 'You don't push him, do you?'

'Certainly,' they said together.

'But you can't push a man about in a Bath chair if you are blind,' I declared.

They laughed—the heartiest laughter I had heard for a long time.

'Listen to him!' cried Mr. Quinn breathlessly. 'Listen to him! He ought to see us bowling along the highroad with motors behind us and motors before us, volley and thunder! How many miles a week do we do, partner?'

'Oh, about twenty-five!' said Mr. Washington. 'You see,' he explained, 'Mr. Quinn and I are partners . . .'

'Not sleeping partners . . .' Mr. Quinn added.

'Very much awake,' said Mr. Washington. 'Well now, I live at one end of the village, and Quinn, here, lives at the other. Now, I'm dying by inches . . .'

'My dear sir,' I began. 'You mustn't talk like that . . .'

'Oh, he's slow about it,' Mr. Quinn assured me. 'He'll live to scrap with me about politics for a long time yet. That's the trouble. If only he'd go I should be able to get a bit of peace.'

'But I won't,' said Mr. Washington smiling, though his large face had a twinge of pain in it. 'I mean to stay as long as possible because, in spite of the thorn in the flesh . . .'

'Meaning me,' said Quinn.

'Life's a wonderful thing! And especially just now with all this beauty and the fields like gold, and the trees . . . ah, the trees!'

'Fiddlesticks!' said Quinn smiling. 'I see nothing beautiful about trees.'

'Well,' said Washington patiently, 'I live at one end of the village, and old Quinn lives as far away as he can. Now, as long as I am alone I can't get out to see anything because my married daughter hasn't any spare time with looking after her children. On the other hand, old Quinn can't travel far without me because the roads are dangerous in these days of motor-cars. Well then, how do we stand alone?'

'Don't begin a political oration, Washington,' said Quinn warningly. 'And it's no use asking how we stand alone, because we stand together, only you always sit because you're too confoundedly lazy—being Capital personified.'

Mr. Washington continued unperturbed. 'How do we stand alone? Well, he lives in his small corner, and I live in mine. Very well, sir. What do we do? My daughter and her husband lift me in here if the weather looks promising, and my son-in-law wheels me down to Mr. Quinn's house. Then Quinn does the pushing—and mighty hard work it is—and I do the steering, and so we strike a partnership, and I get out and he gets out, and I see the scenery and the people on the road, and I tell old Quinn, and so life goes merrily on!'

'Wonderful!' said I with genuine admiration.

'Common sense!' said Quinn.

'Gentlemen,' said I, 'you do good together. You help each other by your partnership, and I am sure you must help others who see you and talk to you, even as you have helped me.'

'Of course,' said Quinn laughing, 'I stand to lose in the business, because when Washington tells me anything or describes it, why, I've only his word for it. When you've gone he may tell me you are a tramp, and of course, I'm bound to believe him, but being a gentleman, I wouldn't!'

'Still,' said Washington, 'it's a good partnership. We get along splendidly till we begin talking politics, and I stand for Capital and he stands for Labour, and when we are going to quarrel we are in danger of being run over by a motor, because I can't argue and steer, and he can't argue and push! So naturally we agree!'

I am no philosopher, but I suppose God has put into the world a few men and women of the Washington and Quinn type for much the same reason as a housewife puts yeast into the dough— to keep it from being sad. Some of us may reach heaven on sermons, commandments, and precepts (though I am by no means sure of this), but I think a little good humour and laughter will at any rate help a few of us to rise thitherwards. I confess that when I had left these heroes, two of the most gracious humorists I have ever met, I felt much more brotherly towards my fellow-men, and I was, I think, a step or two nearer the man I might have been, not because they tried to argue me into goodness, but because their brave goodness bubbled over, and a few precious drops fell on me.

In this mood, therefore, I wandered on, taking no thought where I went or how far, but following that pleasant road through a green world, and chuckling to myself at the memory of those two optimists. True optimism is not the baseless faith of shallow people, it is the practical everyday philosophy of wise men and women. Traced back to its source, it is found to flow from an unshakable belief in God, and in His goodness. We believe the best because we know that God is always working for the best, and that what seems the worst is but the shadow of a cloud—and the cloud His gift of rain without which our thirsty souls must perish.

I was meditating on this philosophy when I saw a little elfish man sitting on a gate. His smooth round chin rested in one hand, and in the other he held a bunch of wild flowers. I think he must have been talking to them, for even when I came near, his head was on one side and he was regarding them in a dreamy way, as a girl might look at a ring on her finger when she thought she was alone. He seemed in no way embarrassed at catching sight of me; but jumping nimbly from the gate, he said, 'I love flowers, don't you?'

'Yes,' I said, 'of course.'

'Lovely, aren't they?'

'Wonderful.'

He looked at me oddly, and I felt that his frankly inquiring eyes were searching my face.

'I'm glad you think so,' he said slowly. 'I think so too. Most people don't. Are you going far?'

I said I had thought of turning back to the village.

'Good,' said he, 'will you let me come with you?'

I replied that I should be glad if he would.

'I often come gathering flowers,' he said. 'I

like doing it. Here's a dandelion, beautiful, isn't it? Yellow! Lovely colour, yellow. Brighter than gold. Much! And every petal made as if there was only one petal in the world. And these butter-cups! I once gathered over a thousand of them. Silly, wasn't it? I always think of slums.'

'Slums?'

'Yes. Poor children without good shoes. There are a lot of poor children. You know that, I suppose?'

'Yes, I do.'

'Isn't it a pity?'

'It is.' Somehow, I hardly knew how to answer his odd questions. He talked away easily and naturally. He was smiling at the flowers all the time.

'I never had any myself,' said he. 'Perhaps it's as well. They wouldn't have known much.'

'Who?' I inquired.

'The children.'

'You mean you haven't had any children of your own?'

He smiled and nodded. 'Yes,' said he. 'I often used to think I'd like to have children of my own. Girls, you know. But they would have been poor, so perhaps it's as well as it is. Here are white dead nettles, little princesses, I think, under green umbrellas. White as ivory. The Book says even Solomon in all his glory was not arrayed like one of these. Have you a lot of money?'

I laughed. I couldn't help it. 'Well, no,' I said. 'I should like more.'

He was serious a moment. 'Yes,' he said darkly,

'I believe you. I should. If I'd a lot of money I'd buy seven fields . . .'

'Why seven?'

He looked at his flowers, holding them at arm's length. He was very thoughtful. 'Seven?' he repeated. 'Why seven? One for every day in the week, of course—and a big one for Sunday. Besides, seven's the perfect number. You see, I've gathered these in sevens—seven buttercups and seven daisies—they're asleep now with being in my hand. See the nightcaps? But they'll wake in the morning. Bless them, they'll wake with the sun and open out, and I shall see them as I'm hammering . . .'

'You are a cobbler?'

'That's all I'm good for. They say I'm a bit simple. Funny they should say that. I don't mind. I let them. I smile. It pleases them to think I'm simple, and we have to make other people happy, haven't we? Don't you think so?'

'Yes,' I said. 'We have to try to please other people.'

'I'm glad you agree. I like you. I should think you know a lot, don't you?'

I shook my head. 'There are thousands of things I don't know,' I replied.

He did not answer. He walked by me down the quiet road, taking little steps, and looking at his shadow. Again he was very serious. Presently he glanced up. 'Isn't it lonely?' he asked.

I said it was.

'I'm glad and sorry.'

'Why?'

'Well,' he answered, 'I'm glad because I want these fields and lanes all to myself. I like to have them lonely so that they seem to be mine. But that's wicked, isn't it? That's being selfish. We ought not to be selfish, ought we? But I'm sorry the road is so empty. I'm sorry there's nobody in the fields, because there ought to be. The cities and towns ought to be empty, and the fields ought to be full of people—full, full of people looking at flowers. There ought to be men here, and women —I loved a woman once, but she didn't understand—and there ought to be children. The grass wouldn't hurt their feet if their shoes were thin. The streets are so hard, aren't they? And if they were here the flowers would talk to them.'

'Do they talk to you?'

'Always. That's why I take them home. You see, the buttercups are closed now. So are the daisies. We ought to speak quietly so's not to wake them. But in the morning when I'm hammering they'll wake. I'll put them in a jar in the window, but out of the sun. They'll speak. But Sir Hugh wouldn't understand.'

'Sir Hugh?'

'The man at the hall. He has a lot of money— but he isn't understanding like you. He rushes about. I think him simple, very simple.'

'But he can't be,' said I gravely. 'Simple people don't make a lot of money.'

He didn't answer. He turned and looked over the dreaming fields, all very quiet. He raised his bunch of common flowers and looked earnestly into them. I wondered how long he would be before he spoke. When he did he seemed to have forgotten my question. 'Lovely flowers,' he said. 'I'm glad you like them, too. Most people haven't time for them. You can't see flowers from a motor-car.' Then he laughed an elfish laugh, not at all the laugh you would have expected from a man of sixty. 'Ah, well,' he said, 'they all think me simple. But am I? What if they are simpler than I am? They dash about making money that makes them miserable. They are all busy doing things. And me? I love flowers! They speak to me. If I'd a lot of money I'd buy seven fields, and I'd have a lot of children gathering flowers . . . and I'd mend their shoes for nothing!'

We parted at the bridge as he said he wished to stay there and watch the fish. So there I left him, and when I reached the inn dinner had been waiting twenty minutes, and Martha was flustered because she had made a special kind of meat-pie, and feared the crust might be a bit hard with having been kept longer than usual. She hoped it would be to my liking, and if it were not I was to ring the bell and Betsey would bring me cold chicken and ham with a salad, or mutton if I cared for it . . . but the pie was beyond reproach, as were the good things which followed, including a cheese-cake with curd as yellow as the pastures round the village.

It would be gone seven o'clock, I should say, when I exchanged tobacco pouches with my host. After thanking Martha for the dinner, the memory of which, I said, would be handed down to posterity with the sole purpose of making the mouths of future generations water, I strolled across the green to a wooden seat under an elm, a sort of grand-stand for the elders of the village.

Cricket was being played on the green, and I did not doubt that it was being played correctly, but at first my thoughts were of the village, one of ten thousand in England, nine out of every ten of them so beautiful that we ought ever to be vigilant that these inheritances of ours, old already, are to grow older as graciously as may be.

Here, then, was the spacious green with a dozen giant elms, fine trees, no doubt, when the Armada was blown to wreckage; the grey spire of the church showing thinly above dark yews shading the last resting place of generations of the old brigade; the pond where the ducks paddled against golden ripples; the War Memorial rising proudly above a mass of flowers; a little house with a couple of poplars standing by the wooden gate; half a dozen white cottages with low gables and tiny dormer windows; a garden of Canterbury bells; and the inn with its benchful of old men, the landlord coming to the door every now and then. Here was the village school hard by the institute. Here were half the folk in the neighbourhood come to watch cricket being played as it was always meant to be played, a friendly, vigorous game for the game's sake, a happy, honest rivalry with no ostentation, no stupid niceties to be wrangled over, a swift, clean game played in the evening sunshine.

The game was worth watching, and some of the spectators were worth listening to. Within half an hour of joining the group under the old elm I was furnished with the names of the players, their life-stories, and other details of much interest. Joe Webster, I was informed, was gardener at the Hall, and a great favourite with Sir Hugh. Jim Anderson had had money left by an uncle in Australia, and money one hasn't earned never does nobody no good. 'Tommie' was a batsman and no mistake, and he could bowl as well as any county player into the bargain. The umpire had been married twice, and his second wife was cousin to the prospective Conservative candidate. Young William, I learnt, was as good a ploughman as you could hope to find, and George, the long stump, old Richard Ingleby's lad, was 'sweet' on Phyllis Newbould, one of the bevy of girls near the institute, and if it wasn't a good match, well, you could eat your hat.

'See that?' asked an old man as the ball was slogged to the boundary, 'hang all your professionals, that's what I say. Give me Harry Lockwood every time. Takes after his father, he do. Old Harry were as fine with a bat as any man that ever walked. I remember—now then, look at *that*! Bless me, if he hasn't done it again. That's fifty-three for us . . .'

'Fifty-three be blowed, Mat,' said a burly farmer next to him. 'It's sixty-two, if it's one! And I'm not so sure Harry ought to hit out so hard. Caution, that's what he needs. There's only another four men, and he wants to have a bit of care . . .'

'Now look here, John Thomas,' said the old man, 'you don't know what you're talking about. Caution be hanged. It's caution what's ruined

this country. Look before you leap, eh? Yes, and
then you find a ditch at the other side of the hedge
—oh, lovely, Harry! Bless the lad, his father would
have given anything to see this. Look before you
leap, and there's sure to be a pool, so you don't
leap at all, that's caution. Well, if you've a bit of
go in you, you clap spurs to your horse, and over
you go, and if you get covered with mud, what's
the odds, you're over, aren't you? Now, look here,
if you could get a politician . . .'

'There now! Middle wicket! What did I tell
you? Out for seventeen!'

'Eh well, I wouldn't have thought it of Harry's
lad. But he played a grand game, and no mistake.
What do *you* say, mister?'

'I agree. I suppose it is often better to take a
risk and gain a bit than risk nothing and gain
nothing,' I said.

'There's wisdom, that's what I say. Nothing
venture, nothing win. That's my motto. That's
what I gave the parson for his book, and he made
me pay a shilling, too. He's a knowing old
bird.'

'Oh?'

'Aye. You'll be a stranger here, like?'

'I suppose I am. Last night was the first night
I slept here.'

'Is that so? Well then, you'll may be not know
we have an astonishing parson? It's a pity he's
away from home, he'd have told you a grand story
of how we built the institute, or rather, how he did.
You should have a word with Tom Wood at Manor
Farm, up past the pond. He'll tell you all about it,

being parson's right-hand man. There's more in parson's head than ever comes out of any politician's. Now look at that! How's that for a catch? It's no use, we'll be beaten as I always said . . .'

'Come, come,' a little, thin man at the other end of the bench piped in. 'It's no sort of use you saying you said we'd lose, 'cos you know you said we'd win. You said it yourself, you know . . .'

Then they fell to arguing about it, and presently I left them. I crossed the green, passing Phyllis (whom they had pointed out to me) and observing that though old Ingleby's lad might possibly have done better at cricket, he was unlikely to do better in matrimony.

Thus I came to the pond where three men were sitting on the grass bank. I thought I would ask them the way to Manor Farm, not, to be quite honest, because I had any intention of calling on Mr. Wood at that hour, but because I have found that a query is often the straightest way to a stranger's heart. Now one of the three was a large man with a red face and sixty years of farming stamped on his features; one was lanky and had a melancholy look till he smiled; and one was a merry little man, rather wiry and with hardly an ounce of flesh to spare. All three were smoking pipes as if by so doing they were solemnly performing a sacred rite. Coming level with them I said, 'Good evening, gentlemen. I am told there is a house hereabouts known as Manor Farm?'

'Yes,' said the large man.

'There is,' said the lanky man.

'We know it,' said the little man.

'You can go up the road and turn to your left,' said the large man.

'Or you can go down the road and take the lane on your right,' said the lanky man.

'Or you can go over Thompson's field,' said the little man blowing a cloud of blue smoke into the air, and adding thoughtfully, 'but Thompson's bull is a rough customer now and then.'

I considered this last piece of information and said that in any case it was rather late to go that evening. 'I believe, however,' I informed them, 'that the gentleman who lives at Manor Farm is a Mr. Wood.'

'Yes,' said the large man.

'He is,' said the lanky man.

'We know it,' said the little man.

The large man stroked his chin thoughtfully, and appeared more greatly concerned about my reaching Manor Farm than I was myself. 'It's mebbe a yard or two farther if you go by the road and turn to the left,' he said, 'but the lane isn't bad walking.'

'You could go down the road and turn to the right,' said the lanky man, 'only you'd mebbe have to climb the gate. The hinges is broken, and it's fastened up with rope.'

'And in any case it wouldn't be much use going either way,' said the little man. 'Mr. Wood isn't at home.'

'Then I don't see that it is much use your going to the trouble of telling me how to go there,' I replied, smiling at the three droll men who were evidently enjoying themselves.

'You asked us the way,' said the large man.

E H

'And we like to oblige a stranger,' said the lanky man.

'All of us,' said the little man.

There was the merest suggestion of humour in their faces.

'I should think,' the large man said reflectively, 'I should think Mr. Wood is taking the air at the moment.'

'And smoking his pipe,' said the lanky man.

'And sitting by the pond,' said the little man, getting up and making his bow.

I returned the bow, and thought it very odd that these ancient schoolboys should take a delight in making fun of me in this delightful way. 'Sir,' I said, 'I am glad to meet you. I was told that next to the parson you know more about the building of the village institute than any one. There seems to be a bit of mystery about this institute, and I should be glad if you could explain it. I believe you had much to do with it.'

'Why, as to that,' Mr. Wood replied, 'I rather think someone has been making a great deal of nothing.'

'No, no, Tom,' said the large man. 'You stuck by the parson when no one else did. We all laughed at you, same as they did at Noah, but we know you were right.'

'You helped to build the institute, Tom,' said the lanky man.

'It was nothing much. The parson is the man. It was his idea, and he carried it through.'

'But he never could have done without you, Tom,' the lanky man insisted.

Mr. Wood inclined his head. 'Well, anyway,' he said, 'the credit goes to the parson who dared to take his jacket off, and all honour to him. You see, mister, we had nowhere for the young folk (nor for the old ones, for that matter) to meet of an evening, and no money to build a room for them. Well, the parson got the notion that we ought to have one, and he talked it over with a few of us, but nobody seemed to think anything to it.'

'Only you, Tom.' said the large man.

'I confess, the idea appealed to me from the first, and I backed him up for all I was worth. We called a meeting in the vestry, and we stuck out in spite of the Jonahs. The parson got an estimate of the cost, but it was something round eleven hundred pounds, and the most we could raise was about two hundred and fifty, may be three hundred with promises. But one thing we had, and that was a bit of land to build on—Sir Hugh saw to that. At first he said the idea was nonsense, but the parson had only to talk to him for twenty minutes to make him change his mind.'

He stopped short as if suddenly conscious that he was betraying himself into too much enthusiasm, but it was plain that the institute was his favourite theme, and he needed little encouragement to go on.

'Well, in the end,' he told me, 'we had another meeting, and everybody said the idea must be dropped, but the parson stood up, very quiet and dignified, and he says, "Gentlemen, we need an institute, and we'll have an institute, even if I have to build it myself." '

'And the joke of it was,' said the lanky man eagerly, 'that he'd built a bit of a summer-house only a year before, and it had fallen to pieces one windy night.'

'So everybody laughed,' said the large man, 'and I was one of them.'

Mr. Wood's pipe had gone out. He pointed it at me as he went on with a tale which I was sure he had told many a stranger in the last three or four years. 'You see, the point the parson drove home was that folk will follow if they have a leader, and he was right. I said he would be, and we proved it over and over again. You never saw a man with such enthusiasm. I goaded him on at the beginning, but before we were half through I had to try to hold him back. I thought that institute would kill him. I had a bit of a struggle to hold him back till after harvest, and as soon as October was fairly in we went up to have a talk with Sir Hugh. Then one fine day all the village came to see the parson with his jacket off. The pair of us began digging the foundations of the institute, and a rare sight it was to see us taking off sods, and measuring up with strings, and when we got fairly down to digging the soil out, one or two young chaps came in the evening—we'd a brazier that gave us all the light we wanted—and started giving a hand with a spade. Well, then, we had a few loads of bricks and some mortar, and the parson began laying a course of bricks, and old John Petersen from Arlington came over the next day and said he'd show him how to lay 'em right.'

'And Martin Cowling came over from Rib-thorpe, and began laughing,' said the lanky man with growing interest, 'only when he saw the parson meant business he grew ashamed and started lending a hand, and in the end the two of 'em built the foundations.'

'Well then' said the large man, 'the parson had an idea. He made everybody give him a saying and a shilling, and he gathered about a thousand of 'em, and had them all made into a little book, and then he made everybody who had given him a saying buy a copy of the book. That was clever, you know. Well, he enlisted the schoolmaster among his supporters, and bless me if *he* didn't send the children all over the countryside selling books to people; Simpson turned out trumps, eh?'

'He did,' Mr. Wood agreed. 'He set to work himself, gathered the young men together, and showed them how to lay bricks. And the parson pretended to make a window-frame and bungled purposely so that Timmy Wetherby lost all patience and said, "Dang it all, man, if we're bound to have an institute, we'd better have windows that won't fall out!" That was just what the parson wanted, and Wetherby made 'em all himself, and the doors too. Of course we had a bazaar, and raised nearly a hundred and fifty pounds . . .'

'And Sir Hugh gave another fifty to show willing,' said the lanky man.

'And Sid Wentworth—he's a farmer out Wal-sington way—paid for the slates, and lent three of his hands for putting them on,' said the large man.

'Then Harry—young Harry—got a few fellows together, and they clubbed up, and undertook to make the wooden partitions and to paint the whole place inside and out,' the lanky man added.

'And a good job they made of it, too,' said the large man.

'And so,' said Mr. Wood, 'the thing grew of itself, and Sir Hugh opened it at Whitsuntide, and a cosier spot you couldn't find anywhere. And, as the parson said all along, you've only to lead, and others will follow.'

'All we like sheep,' commented the lanky man, lighting his pipe and standing up to go. 'It's after ten,' he remarked abruptly. 'Good night.'

The other two followed for it was later than they had thought; before I could say more than a few words they were off into the blue night, leaving me to walk slowly across the green and by the neat institute, and the vicarage where lived the astonishing parson, a born leader of men, as Mr. Wood had said. But I thought that Mr. Wood had forgotten to tell me one thing, for he had said nothing of the man who, by his faith and loyalty, had made it possible for the parson to go on. That man had been Mr. Wood himself, who had perhaps never realized how easily a man may lead ten thousand if he have but one to lean on. Who knows but that it was to the fidelity (and perhaps for the praise) of some long-forgotten soldier in the camp that Alexander the Great owed all his mighty conquests? It is our faith in a man which often makes him strong, our expectation which enables him to do the impossible.

And so I came to the inn and went to bed thinking there might be much folly in the world but that at any rate there was a little wisdom. I remembered Longfellow's:

> Something attempted, something done,
> Has earned a night's repose,

and on this pleasant thought I fell asleep, my window open to the wind and stars and all the freshness of the summer night.

CHAPTER III

I begin the day with breakfast in the kitchen; read Thomas à Kempis in the open air; learn something from a mender of fences; think about grass, and the universe which somehow seems to have a twist in it; sit by a philosophical angler; talk with a lady who loved mending socks; and go to bed early at Beulah Cottage.

I WAS ON the road by seven o'clock next morning. My landlord was an early riser, and, at my request, he and I had breakfast together in the brick-floored kitchen with the sunshine streaming through the open door, and John humming as he worked in the entrance. I paid my reckoning, begged my host to give my respects to his wife, slipped a piece of silver into John's hand, wrote a rhyme in the visitors' book, and took an uphill road out of the village.

I had prayed no prayer that morning, but when I came to the hilltop I took out serious Thomas à Kempis, and sat down with him on a heap of stones where I read:

'If there be joy in the world, surely a man of a pure heart possesseth it. And if there be anywhere tribulation and affliction, an evil conscience best knoweth it. As iron put into the fire loseth its rust, and becometh clearly red hot, so he that wholly turneth himself unto God putteth off all slothfulness, and is transformed into a new man. When a man beginneth to grow lukewarm, then he is afraid of a little labour, and willingly receiveth comfort from outward things. But when he once beginneth to overcome himself perfectly and to walk manfully in the way of God, then he esteemeth those things to be light which before seemed grievous unto him.'

Then I prayed in the fresh air, prayed that I might manfully walk in the way of God, and that I might do it—as Thomas himself suggests on an earlier page—by simplicity and purity. I imagine these are two words which make little appeal to men and women of this age. They have a flavour of the monastery rather than of the market-place. Simplicity does not get a man far in business. Purity of thought is not acceptable at the club. But then, I do not know that Thomas was thinking of business, nor was he troubled about the figure we may cut at our club. He was thinking of the life of the spirit, that deep, essential part of our being which lives (if it is to live at all) by a simple faith, and of that purity of thought by which alone we can come close to God, learning His will, and trying to do it.

Now these thoughts were my companions up and down the hill and along a dozen miles of road with trees here and there. It was an odd thing, or so it seemed, that I should find a philosopher early in the day. 'You are mending a fence?' I asked.

'Yes,' said he, 'I am mending it, though that isn't how I should describe it myself.'

'Oh?'

'I'd say I was keeping it young—and that's

another way of saying I'm not letting it grow old. It's pretty much the same thing—with a difference.'

'But you are an old man yourself,' I said.

He drove a stake into the ground, leaned on it, and looked at me out of a pair of moist eyes. 'An old man, am I?' he asked. 'Old? Well, now mister, if it's a fair question, how old would you say I am?'

I considered before replying, looking more carefully at this countryman with his brown, wrinkled face framed in white whiskers. I noted the happiness in his eyes, and the whimsical smile about his lips.

'I think you have seen at least seventy summers,' I told him.

'Nearer eighty,' he replied.

'Then you *are* an old man.'

He shook his head. 'Five hours and a bit,' said he after consulting a large silver watch.

'Five hours and a bit? How is that?'

'I was up just before six this morning,' said he, 'and, as my custom is, I knelt down by my bed, and I prayed; and the Lord made a new man of me, repairing me same as I'm repairing this old fence.'

'Then you are not old?'

'Not I. My body is old, and half filled with aches and pains, for sciatica plagues me now and then. But, bless your life, sir, a man isn't his body. That's only the earthly temple of the spirit, and no matter how old the clay may be, a man is young if his spirit never grows old.'

'And how shall a man keep his spirit young?'

'By repairing it continually as I am repairing this fence.'

'And how are you doing that?'

He smiled. 'Why, sir,' said he, 'surely you know how to repair a fence. There be two things to do, and two things only. I take out the worn timber and replace it with sound stakes. I change the old for new.'

I nodded. 'Yes,' I said, 'I can see you are preparing sound stakes, and I understand all that very plainly, but how does a man repair his life so that even at eighty years of age he is still young?'

'How is it that this fence, over a hundred years old, has not a bit of timber in it that has stood half that time? And for myself, sir, why every day I take out of my mind whatever is unwholesome— or I should say I have it taken out for me.'

'How?'

'By prayer. Every night I am still for a bit.'

'But it is not always easy to be still. I have little time for doing nothing.'

'Ah, but a man isn't doing nothing if he is waiting on the Lord. That is praying, and God can do anything with a man on his knees. He can do anything with any of us when we'll let Him.'

'You let Him?'

'To be sure. A man cannot go through the day without a bit of himself rotting, so every night I ask that the rottenness may be cut away as I cut out the rotting wood in this fence.'

'And in the morning?'

'In the morning, sir, I go down on my knees

again—except when the sciatica's very bad and won't let me do it—and I pray for a right spirit to be renewed within me. I ask for new power to serve and to do right, and for new grace, and new and stronger faith, and a new vision of God in place of the old one that sometimes grows dim. It always comes. I am born again every day, and though the outward body decay, the inward spirit keeps young—aye, younger now than half-a-century ago, and a man may say continually that it is good to be alive.'

So he talked, this simple, old-fashioned, God-fearing man, and I wondered greatly that in the twentieth century this simplicity and purity should still be found. I suppose one of my clever friends who has argued religion and prayer out of life could knock this old man's logic into nothing in five minutes. I dare say the psychologists would make short work of his devotions—merely self-induced consciousness. This one thing I know, that whereas I was blind, I began to see, for this old man with his radiant youth lent me a bit of sunshine, and sent me on my way one hair's breadth nearer a Christian. Not a great achievement I admit, but something.

Besides, how wonderful that an English road should thus bring me to a spiritual experience! Nor was that the end, for when I had walked a little farther, I looked about me and saw the wonder of the road. Some of you have never seen an English road. It is more than dust or tarmacadam. It is a living praise. Did I not speak of its wonder to that disgruntled young man?

Yet how much of its loveliness and charm I omitted to mention! My feet, walk as carefully as I would on the grass verge, my feet must needs crush the golden chalices of the buttercups. I saw the fool's parsley like little white parasols for the fairies. There were the yellow cradles of the ladies' fingers, the purple mitres of the clover, the nodding heads of the ribwort plantains, the long trailing stems of the vetch (too weak to stand alone), its pods like aerial canoes, its hair-like tendrils making spirals up to God. I ran my fingers through the grasses, many of them already seeding; and down I sat among them.

After air and water and rocks, is there anything more common than grass? It grows in cold and hot lands, over forgotten cities, above the remains of vanished civilizations. It is the last blanket for rich and poor. The slightest breeze sets it quivering, the greatest hurricane cannot destroy it. It feeds the cattle on a thousand hills. Cultivate it, and it is the bread you eat and the sugar for your tea.

Within a square yard of the green border by the road I found not one sort of grass only, but perennial ryegrass, Italian ryegrass, cocksfoot, meadow fescue, hard fescue, sheep's fescue, tall fescue, crested dogstail, Timothy, rough meadow grass, meadow foxtail, and tall oatgrass. There was also red and white clover and trefoil which, I suppose, hardly come under the botanist's term, though every seed-merchant includes them with his list of grasses.

It would appear that grass is not just grass—

a garment for Mother Earth which to-day is, and to-morrow is cast into the oven; but a mixture of living things, each individualistic, and all combining to keep the world fresh and green, to support life, and to enable the poet to write his rhymes, the politician to make his promises, and the lover to dream his dreams.

A farmer friend of mine first told me of the marvels of grass-seeds. It was he who explained that there are millions of blades of cockshott grass to the acre, that every stem has scores of glumes, and that every glume is exquisitely fashioned, its serrated sheath royal purple in colour. A score of darrel seeds will not cover your little finger-nail, but each has the will to strike down into the earth and up to the sun. Strangest of all, in every handful of seed are what are known as 'hard' seeds, perhaps only one or two. They are exceptions to a rule. Nature says that when a seed falls into the ground it must die and then grow, and nine hundred and ninety-nine seeds out of every thousand do so. But the odd one does not. It lies dormant through spring and summer, through autumn and winter. Perhaps a year passes, or two years may pass, and still the hard seed lies unchanged. Then, one day, it stirs and grows. It is Nature's way of keeping a reserve which comes up after the anticipated crop, so that, should some exceptional catastrophe destroy the young grass, the species may not be annihilated. The danger passed, the odd seeds will come up here and there, scattering new life again! Business men may be interested to learn that the principle of providing reserve capital for emergency use is one of Nature's oldest institutions.

All this I turned over in my mind as I sat by the roadside. I lit my pipe and thought of the wonder of it all, realizing that this provision Nature makes with the grasses, something so unexpected, is but another proof that logic does not always bring us to the truth. The universe—if you will forgive me for saying so—is not quite a straightforward, honest-to-goodness affair. There is a twist in it.

Smith, a friend of mine, has a phrase which often irritates me. He says, 'There you are! It is as plain as a pikestaff, and *it follows logically* . . .'

But why logically? I stood up and took to the road again, considering this problem as I walked.

Every dabbler in elementary physics knows that a decrease in temperature is accompanied by a definite ratio of contraction. He can give you the scientific law concerning this phenomenon. When the temperature of a bar of iron decreases, the bar contracts; when mercury loses heat, its volume diminishes; the cooler air becomes, the more easily is it forced into a small space. This law applies to almost every common substance, and one might *logically* conclude that it applies to water, which, indeed, it does, till the temperature is round about four degrees centigrade. Then the law breaks down, for water at that point begins to expand. Logically it should not. Actually it does.

Any schoolboy will tell you the earth is round, but if you come to measure it very accurately you find that it is slightly flattened at the Poles. Smith could hardly have anticipated this. Or, to take another example, Smith might argue that as a man appears to be symmetrical, having an ear on one side, and a similar ear on the other, an arm, a leg, and an eye on the left side, and similar members on the other, therefore *logically* it is as plain as a pikestaff that he will have two hearts, one on the left side, and the other on the right. That is precisely where Smith's logic leads him astray.

My friend, and other reasonable people, examining a brick (preferably one of those I find when digging in my garden), might argue very cleverly that if a brick is a brick, half a brick is half a brick, and a quarter of a brick is a quarter of a brick, and so on and so on. It is all as plain as a pikestaff till you have reduced my brick to molecules, and from molecules to atoms, and from atoms to electrons, and then in a flash my brick becomes radiant energy, force, a knot in the all-pervading ether; indeed, according to Professor Jeans, not a brick at all but a permanent illusion, or a materialistic form of imagination! Where are we then? Where is my friend and his pikestaff, which, for anything he knows, may be a ripple in the hypothetical continuum! My friend himself may be synthesized into a cosmic dream, a four-dimensional nightmare.

Now, these things are beyond me. I leave Smith to wrestle with them, if he can lay hands on them. I look at Nature and find that she never makes two things alike. One pea in a pod looks pretty much the same as another, but if you plant one it will produce four flowers, and the other five.

Always there is a difference, and the glory of it is that you cannot possibly anticipate the difference either inductively or deductively. It happens so— not, I think, by a breaking down of a great law, but in accordance with a greater law than Smith knows of, a law so great that it includes exceptions.

When you think of it, how astonishing it is that fish in the warm seas of a thousand million years ago (my friend talks in thousands and millions as if he were a banker, or a government official) have not remained fish to this very day. If I were a logician I should say, once a fish, always a fish. It would not have occurred to me that by the process of evolution fish might quite naturally become reptiles, and birds, and elephants, and men, and even Smiths. Knowing something of my friend's genealogical tree (he had, I believe, an ancestor who intended sailing in the *Mayflower*, but changed his mind) I should not have *logically* deduced that he was descended from the fishy inhabitants of the primeval sea; at any rate it would not have been as plain as a pikestaff to me.

Logic and science alone will never help me to fathom all the mysteries of the universe, or the depths of my own nature. For my universe is unreasonable, and I, myself, am a paradox. My universe has a twist in it, and a glorious twist. It can never be dull, and I can never index it com-pletely. Life is continually surprising me, but I am not surprised that I should be surprised. I expect to be. And when I begin meditating about life and the framework of it, I find my reason and

F H

logic totally inadequate to help me to reach out and grasp God's hand; but my faith teaches me to feel His hand on my shoulder. Smith's logical arguments rule God out of His own universe, and wash out the nail-prints from human life. I cannot bring God back by logic, but I can read Him everywhere by faith. Besides, love *knows* without arguing.

All this thinking took me several miles up hill and down till I came to a valley with poplars like green spires on the low hills beyond, and a stream flowing by many hawthorns. Having food with me, I chose a pleasant spot in a meadow above the stream, and there with two thieves I shared tomato sandwiches and half a cheesecake, gifts of the landlord's wife. The thieves were a pair of hedgesparrows which came forward boldly to steal the crumbs, and I confess I was sorry that they should steal from one who was willing to give.

Now, while I had been resting, I had caught sight of someone farther up the stream. I took him to be an angler, for he had a rod and line, but he sat so still that I began to think he must have fallen asleep. At last, curiosity getting the better of me, I strolled along the bank till I was within a yard or two of him. He had looked neither to the right nor the left, and I do not think he was aware of my presence till he heard my approach. I stopped short. 'It is a lovely day,' I remarked.

He nodded.

I was not sure whether to go on or stay where I was, for I doubted how far custom and courtesy would permit me to intrude on a stranger's privacy. However, I ventured to ask if he had caught anything. He said, 'No.'

This was not encouraging. I could see he was not a countryman. The city was stamped on him, and one glance at his thin face, the strong jaw, the thin lips, the bright, rather humorous eyes behind horn-rimmed spectacles, suggested that he had a swivel-chair in a large office, and said to many, 'Do this,' and they would do it. So, taking my courage in both hands, I said, 'May I sit down here?'

He regarded me searchingly before replying curtly, 'Yes, if it is more comfortable than standing.'

This was not a very pressing invitation, but I thought I saw the ghost of a smile about his lips, so I thanked him very deliberately, and sat down. Then I said, 'Sir, you do not seem to be having very good sport.'

'On the contrary,' said he, 'I have been doing very well till the last few minutes.'

'But you have not caught any fish.'

'Only one,' said he, 'and a rather queer one.'

I love a man with a sense of humour. I told him candidly that I had been watching him for some time. 'I never saw you bait a hook or flick your rod,' I said. 'I confess it made me curious.'

'I am sorry to have wasted so much of your time,' said he.

'It is regrettable,' I said. 'But what about *your* time?' Then, as I was lounging on the grass, idly smoking my pipe, I made bold to add, 'How comes it, sir, that in strenuous days you have time to spend in this unprofitable way?'

'I repeat,' said he, 'only the last few minutes have been unprofitable.'

'You would rather be alone?'

'That was why I came here,' he replied, but he was quick to add, 'No, there is no need for you to go.' Then, in a very simple and rather winsome manner, he began to talk about himself, telling me he was a business man employing scores of people. I gathered that he took some share in the civic life of a big town. He told me he had five children approaching manhood and womanhood. He said that during most days in the year he was busy going to and fro and doing this and that. 'I suppose it is only natural to be caught up in the whirl of life,' he said, speaking very quietly and looking at the slow stream all the time. 'I do not regret it. I think I love it. There is so much to do, or we think so, and apparently so little time in which to get it done. My life seems crowded with action. I am like a builder hurriedly putting one stone on another, carrying the edifice up higher and higher. Now and then I feel I must get down from the scaffold and stand a few yards from the work of my hands and look at it carefully. It is the only way to be sure it is straight and true and beautiful.'

'And to do that you take to fishing?'

'*Thinking*,' he corrected. 'To change the metaphor, it does not matter how quickly you run, you will never get to the winning-post if you are going in the wrong direction. I take a day off now and then to let the dust settle so that I can see which way I am going, and to give myself a chance to look beyond the immediate to the future.'

'From being active you become passive?'

'That sums it up very well. I like to examine myself, and make sure I am doing the right things, and that I am keeping the right relationships between myself and others—my wife, my children, my employees, and so on. You understand?'

'I think so.' I glanced at him, this very practical, I should say rather hard-headed, business man, and I said, 'I remember that Jesus went apart to pray.'

He did not reply, but after a pause he said, 'I am a great believer in silence.'

So for a minute or two we spoke no word, and presently I broke the silence by saying, 'I think I understand why you cultivate the art of being still, an art which, I am afraid, is in danger of being lost. But why bring a rod and line? Why not come into the country with your hands in your pockets?'

He smiled rather oddly, and it was not altogether a happy smile. 'Life is pretty complicated,' he explained. 'I am afraid some of the folk at home, and most of the rest of the people who know me, would think me mentally affected if I came into the country with no objective. They would be sorry for me. No, it may be cowardly, but it is distinctly safer to come fishing—ostensibly.'

I stood up. 'Yes,' I said, 'perhaps it is. The trouble is that fools like me are apt to disturb meditations. Please forgive me. I see that you are not wasting your time, and I could wish with all my heart that other people would practise this art of yours. It might help us all to go a little way towards putting the wrong things right. Perhaps even the politicians might get something done if they learnt how to do nothing successfully.'

'It is within the bounds of possibility,' he murmured, 'but only just. Anyhow, I hope they won't all take to fishing.'

After a few more words with him I crossed the meadow to the road. I knew he wished to be alone with his thoughts; and the best apology I could give him for breaking in on his privacy was to leave him in peace. But I could not readily forget him, and somehow I linked him with the old mender of fences, for surely both were builders of the New Jerusalem.

If the angler was glad to be rid of me, I was not sorry to be on the way to a resting-place for the night, for I had walked a good many miles, and though the afternoon was young and the children had been left school no more than an hour or so, I determined to find a bed in the next village.

I found it sooner than I had expected. Before I was in the heart of the village I came to a cottage in a garden with the flowers our grandmothers loved. There was a green fence round the garden, and a gate with the word 'Beulah Cottage.' It was the old-fashioned name which took my fancy at once. I opened the gate and walked up a path hemmed in with lupins as closely as the way guarded by lions along which Christian went, trembling. I raised my hand to knock on a half-open door, but before my hand came down a pleasant voice said, 'Come in, love.'

Oddly enough, the invitation kept me outside. I hesitated. Then I knocked again and heard the voice say, 'Come in, John.'

Now, they do not call me John—though John is a good name for a man. So I said, 'It isn't John—it's me.'

Then there was the rustling of a skirt (I had visions of a duchess in black silk and diamonds) and a white-haired lady with a fresh complexion and blue eyes came to the door, and laughed, and said in a delightfully natural way (as if she had known me all my life), 'There now, whatever will you think of me? I thought it was John coming with the eggs. I'm so sorry. I just caught sight of *somebody* at the gate.'

'John must be a handsome fellow,' said I.

She laughed again.

'The fact is,' I explained, 'I was wondering if you ever put any one up for the night. You see, I saw the name on the gate, and I thought whoever lived here must be very pleasant, and if you could give me a bed . . .'

She looked me up and down with friendly eyes. 'Yes,' she said, 'I do have a visitor or two sometimes. You can stay and welcome, but you have come the day before baking day, so you'll have to make do with what I have.'

'Excellent!' said I. 'It will be heavenly!'

'I don't know,' she said. 'I'm not sure they have ham in heaven.'

Then she led me indoors. There was a charming

kitchen with a big oven and a wood fire (though the day was warm) and a sunny parlour with a piano, a bamboo table, an aspidistra, and a family Bible. There was a wonderful little staircase, very steep and narrow, to a small yellow bedroom with open rafters in the sloping roof, and a spray of vine venturing six inches in at the little window. There was an iron bedstead with a feather bed, a picture of the Angelus, and a text which said, 'Come unto me, and I will give you rest.'

When she had shown me my bed she rustled downstairs to cook something, and I stood in the little room and read the text, and listened to the swallows which had nests under the eaves, and felt that here was a bit of Old England unspoiled by the march of progress.

I went downstairs to find a table laid for me in the parlour where a fox-terrier was on guard by the chair I was to sit in. He followed me into the garden, and my hostess kept coming to the door and running back to the fire to fry ham and eggs—for John had brought the eggs, and the news.

When all was ready my gracious hostess left me to dine alone, but when I had finished she allowed me to dry the 'things' in the scullery, and said I could sit and smoke in the garden, and she would come with me if I didn't mind her mending stockings and socks. I had no objection on that score, but when she came I wondered to see her work-basket with a dozen pairs of socks.

'Is there a big family somewhere?' I ventured to ask from my retreat near the raspberry canes. 'Where do you hide them all?'

She laughed her delightfully natural laugh. 'Oh, I don't hide them anywhere,' she said. 'There aren't any to hide. They are just neighbours' socks and stockings.'

'Oh?'

She rummaged in her work-basket for some wool. She was talking pleasantly all the time. 'You see,' she explained, 'everybody doesn't care for darning, and I do. I love it. And everybody hasn't time. There seems so much to do to-day, doesn't there? I sometimes think we all have less time at our finger-ends now than ever before. So a few of the people in the village bring me their socks and stockings to darn, and I just love doing it.'

'I see.' I was looking at her as she worked away, her eyes on a sock without a heel. I wondered if here was the third 'mender' I had met in the day— fences, characters, socks! I think perhaps she felt I was looking at her, for she glanced up inquiringly. 'I am sure it is very good of you to do it,' I said. 'The village folk must bless you in their going out and coming in.'

She smiled.

'You have many friends, I suppose?'

'Yes. People are often coming to see me.'

'So you are not lonely?'

'Oh, no. At least, not often.'

'Just sometimes? In the winter evenings perhaps?'

'Well, sometimes. Still, it doesn't do to think about one's self too much, does it? And, of course, I have so much to be thankful for. Besides, we can't ever be really lonely, can we?'

'I don't know,' I said. 'Sometimes we can be very lonely indeed.'

'Not if we believe the promise. You know what we are told. "Lo, I am with you alway, even unto the end." It is a great word of comfort, don't you think so?'

'I do.'

She had let her hands rest in her lap—the needle half in and half out of a row of stitches. 'Perhaps I'm a bit old-fashioned,' she said quietly. 'But I *feel* His presence so wonderfully. He often comes into the scullery with me. I never feel ashamed of His seeing me with my coarse apron on. He understands. You see, I just trust Him, so I know it's all right. I used to worry a lot years ago, but now I find it all so simple. All you have to do is to take Him at His word.'

I wondered if perhaps I might inquire what had happened years ago, but when I saw the gentleness in her face—with its shadow behind the smile—and looked again at the white hair, I was afraid. So I let the chance go by, and I was not really sorry when two girls—they would be about seventeen or eighteen—came into the garden to talk to her, calling her 'Mother Hubbard' in a charming way, and nodding to me shyly. I thought perhaps they would be jollier without a stranger, so I excused myself, and went upstairs to bed.

But not to sleep, for the sun was still in the sky. I lay in bed, Thomas à Kempis in my hand, and I heard laughter outside, and I saw the sun glinting like gold on the bevelled edge of the little painted mirror, and I felt a peace steal into my heart. I opened Thomas at random, and he said, 'Meddle not with things too high for thee,' which was rather more assertive and rather less gentle than usual; and yet, unoffended, I meditated on it. After all, there was much in it. Science bewilders. Theology confounds. But my hostess in her simplicity had a trustfulness that, at any rate, was more useful to her than scepticism. So, after musing, I fell asleep.

CHAPTER IV

I meet an organ-blower who believed in Providence; am shown the treasures of an old church; chop firewood; have dinner with a vicar; hear about a best-seller that was never published; and am told the strange story of a phantom.

M<small>Y</small> HOSTESS had already 'bustled round' and made everything ship-shape when I went downstairs in the morning. We sat down to breakfast, and I learnt that the 'milk boy's' father was making hay while the sun shone, and that his brother had caught a young owl the night before, and hoped to tame it. Dora White, I learned, always 'popped' in as she went to catch her 'bus for the town, and that morning she had worn a new frock she had made herself. My hostess smiled and said she rather thought Dora had an admirer, anyhow, she'd seen Robert Parkby standing near the churchyard gate three Sundays running. Also the vicar had been in to have a word with her.

'What?' I asked, glancing at the clock on the mantelpiece, 'a call from the clergy before nine?'

'Oh, yes, that's nothing. He's an early riser. He was here soon after eight.'

'Energetic man,' I murmured.

'He's a dear,' said my hostess, pouring coffee from a brown jug. 'Two pieces?'

'Please.' I stirred my coffee. 'You don't need a morning paper here,' I observed. Then, thinking of the vicar, I said, 'I suppose you don't write the vicar's sermons for him?'

'Oh, no,' she laughed. 'I just take the Sunday school, that's all.'

'All of it?'

'There isn't much.'

'And mend socks?'

She laughed. 'The coffee's going cold,' she said. 'You ought to see the vicar before you go. He's a wonderful man, and tragedy has made his life beautiful. He's only about forty now, and he lost his wife about three years ago. He's so bright and cheerful, and she was such a lovely woman.' She paused. 'I think,' she said slowly, 'he is the bravest man I know.'

'Perhaps I shall meet him,' I said. 'I think if you could do with me for another meal, I might look round the village this morning and perhaps call on the vicar.'

She said I could stay, and welcome.

With a vague intention of going to see the church, I strolled into the village, found my way to a small square where the 'buses stopped, saw an old inn with wisteria growing up to the chimney, bought a newspaper at Mr. Jordan's little shop where you could buy chocolate, bananas, potatoes, camera films, feeding bottles, and pills; and overtook an old man on the green. He walked with his legs far apart, and leaned heavily on a knotted cudgel. Of him I inquired the way to the church.

He stood still, looked at me with grave eyes, leaned a little more heavily on his stick, and replied, 'Do you believe in Providence?'

I said I did.

He seemed relieved. Putting his cudgel under his arm, and gripping the collar of his jacket with both hands as if to hold himself down, he said, 'I'm glad to hear it. I believe in Providence myself. I always have done, and I always shall. It's Providence that guides our feet into the way of truth.'

'Yes,' I said. 'I think you are right. I should be glad . . .'

'Mebbe you would,' said he, 'but it isn't a matter of *thinking* I'm right, it's a matter of *knowing*, that's what it is. Thinking don't come into matters of the soul. Faith is more than thinking.'

I wondered if he would tear the collar from his coat, for every sentence was punctuated with a heavy jerk. 'Very true,' I said, 'very true. We were speaking about the church, and perhaps you would be kind enough to tell me the way.'

'Mister,' said he, 'it's plain that Providence directed you to me, for seeing you don't know your way about this village, it would have been easy for you to have come here and not found me standing on the green. But here I am when required, just as if I might have been waiting for you. You might have asked Mrs. Hatfield the way, and the Lord knows she might have snapped your head off, her being worried to death what with the shop, and her husband, and everything. You might have gone to the house next door and asked the poor old body there, but bless you, she'd never have told you what you wanted to know. And why? Because the Lord in His mercy, in ways past our poor understanding, appointed it unto her to be stone deaf. Or you might have knocked at the door of that house at the far end of the green, and if you *had* knocked there would have been no answer, for my missus had gone down to Jordan's to buy a bit of something for dinner, and you can reckon on her being away a good hour. Women *will* talk, you know. So *she* wouldn't have heard you, and no more should I, for here I am on the green. But no, Providence ordained that your feet should come to me, and though it don't do to boast, boasting not being a Christian virtue, I don't mind saying you couldn't have come to nobody more likely to help you than me, for I'm the organ-blower.'

'Then,' said I, 'perhaps you will tell me the way to the church.'

He shook his head. 'No,' he said. 'I'll do more than *tell* you. I'll go along with you, for it is written that if a man bid thee go with him a mile, go with him twain.' (It was on the tip of my tongue to explain that I had not asked him to go a mile with me, but I refrained.)

'And in life,' said the preacher, 'it isn't enough to be a signpost, just pointing the way to right-eousness. We have to walk that way ourselves, and I've been walking in it turned sixty-seven years, mister, though the old legs is a bit stiff now.'

By this time we had begun making a move in what I presumed was the direction of the church. 'You must have patience with an old man, mister,' he said, hobbling along painfully, 'we're none of us as young as we used to be.'

'Then do not trouble to come with me,' I said.
'If you will tell me the way, I will hurry on alone.'

'No, no,' said he, 'that would be a pity, for
when you got there you'd have to wait for me.
You see, mister, I am the prop that supports the
church.' He stopped to take breath. 'That may
sound like boasting, but it isn't boasting, it's
telling a plain fact. You see, I blows the organ,
and if I didn't where should we be then?'

I could not think, so I did not risk a reply.

'Where should we be then?' he repeated. 'The
organ won't play without me blowing. Our Mr.
Thomas is a very fine man, and knows a lot about
music, and his wife keeps bees; but I tell you,
when he sits down at the organ and pulls out the
stops, and gets his music right way up, and starts
off, why, bless you, there's not a sound comes from
that there organ if I happen to be having a word
with Joe Harris, and ain't working the handle.'

'How remarkable.'

'No, sir, not remarkable a bit, only natural, for
an organ won't play without wind no more than
a man can do good work without breath, nor live
by faith without the spirit of the Lord in him.' He
stood still again. 'The devil's a knowing gentleman,' he declared.

I did not quite see the connexion, so I asked how
he knew.

'Well,' said he, 'Joe Harris is a decent fellow,
and sings tenor—I used to myself, but I'm mighty
short of breath nowadays. He is all smiles and full
of news, but he is a snare unto my path, and a
temptation I am called upon to resist, for the Lord

appointed me to blow the organ, and it isn't for me to go listening to Joe Harris, 'specially when the vicar's praying about the royal family, and Joe has nothing to do between singing Amen but lean back again' my curtain, and tell me a bit of news about what's going on, and me prone to listen to him when my plain duty is to blow like the walls of Jericho. There's not a night goes by without me getting on my bended knees and praying for deliverance from Joe Harris.'

He fumbled for his handkerchief, and wiped the perspiration from his forehead. 'I try to do my duty, mister,' he said, 'and a man can't do fairer than that. I take it as a great honour to blow the organ, and sometimes me and Mr. Thomas puts that much beef into the psalms till you would think you were listening to the heavenly host. I reckon I've blown many a soul into heaven, but mark you, mister, I am only a humble organ-blower.'

Again he stood still, and sighing deeply, he said, 'But times aren't going to be what they was. There is some talk of getting a new-fangled engine to blow the organ, but may the Lord keep it out of the church till my blowing days are done. You can never expect folk to hear the angels singing if the organ's blown with an engine. Our Mr. Thomas has set his mind on one, and the day will come, but Providence won't let me down. It's a wonderful thing, Providence. If a man stops . . .'

By this time we had come to the churchyard gate. A look of bewilderment came into his fine old face. He put his hand into the back pocket of his trousers, felt in the pockets of his jacket, looked

G H

troubled for a moment, and then smiled serenely.
'No,' he said, more to himself than to me, 'it's not
Providence that's to blame, it's man's folly and
pride. Drat it all, I could have sworn I had that
there key on me, but I've gone and left it at home.
There is nothing for it, mister, but us going back
to fetch it. Mebbe it's discipline, same as the
Israelites suffered for forty years in the wilderness.'

We looked at one another and laughed. I was
quite prepared to walk back with the old fellow,
for it was a delight to hear him talk, but we had
scarcely reached the gate (the one where Dora's
admirer had a habit of waiting hopefully) when a
tall man came across the churchyard. 'The vicar,'
said my guide. 'And the door isn't unlocked at
this time of day! Very particular, he is, to have it
open.'

'Good morning, William,' said the vicar cheerily.
He had a friendly nod for me.

'Excuse me,' said William apologetically, 'you
don't happen to have your key on you, do you? I
was just going to show this gentleman round the
church, only I've come without me key.'

'Oh, that's all right, William. I have mine.
There are twelve gates into the New Jerusalem,
you'll remember!'

'Aye, aye, praise the Lord, and there'd need be
wi' such daft 'uns coming along as me.'

The vicar opened the priest's door. 'Interested
in churches?' he asked, addressing me.

'Very,' I said. 'I think they are the treasure-
houses of our land.'

I saw a flush of pleasure suffuse his pale face.

'I agree,' he said. 'It is a delight to meet any one who thinks so. You'll see the stone over the door?'

'It looks Norman,' I said, 'a series of circles for eternity, probably.'

'Excellent! Precisely what I've always said myself, but few people here understand these things. Come in, come in, we have much that is worth seeing inside. A fine old church, isn't it?' He waved his hand to indicate the interior. 'You see the oak roof-beams? All hewn before Elizabeth's day, the marks of the adze still on them. See the king-posts, and the shield carved on the wallplate? You may recognize the arms as those of one of the oldest families hereabouts. The first Sir Ninian came over with the Conqueror, the last died fighting at Flodden Field. There was another who fought side by side with Henry the Fifth at Agincourt, and came home to double his estate by marrying a descendant of John of Gaunt, Shakespeare's time-honoured Lancaster, you remember. Do you mind coming this way?'

I obeyed. The polite vicar who had nodded to me in the churchyard had become an enthusiastic antiquarian, grateful, I thought, for an opportunity of showing someone round the church of which he was evidently proud. He led me to a large stone altar tomb with crocketed panels, and alabaster figures of a knight and his lady. The knight had a sword at his side, and his hands in prayer, his hair curling under his helmet, and his coat-of-mail drawn in by a beautifully embroidered belt. The lady, in a long robe and a rich headdress like a coronet, had a little dog at her feet.

In the panels round the tomb were gracious figures of a son dressed very much like his father, and seven daughters, one of whom was a nun.

'Beautiful craftsmanship,' said the vicar, running his hand over one of the alabaster figures. 'Here is the last Sir Ninian but one. He has been sleeping in the chancel over 400 years. He would attend service in this church, and an antiquarian friend of mine declares that he was baptized at the old font; you will see it in the corner near the tower. The new one is an abomination, and if only one had money enough I should give myself the pleasure of breaking it with a hammer. It is moving to think of this knight coming to church with his wife, the two of them praying here so long ago. You will see that one of his daughters entered a convent, but the boy, the last Sir Ninian, evidently believed in fighting. He had a monument here till the days of the Commonwealth, but Cromwell is said to have stabled his horses in the nave, and the soldiers are believed to have smashed his alabaster figure. A fragment of it was used for patching up the south chapel wall. It is a miracle that this tomb should have been spared. But we have something more precious.' He took out his keys, and opened the vestry door. Pointing to a window, he said, 'What do you think of that for old glass?'

'Wonderful,' I exclaimed.

He had stepped back to see what effect this revelation would have on me. 'You can go twenty miles without finding anything to equal it,' he assured me. 'But I doubt if half a dozen people in the village realize its value. Your friend who forgot his key, thinks nothing of it, and is of the opinion that if this dark stuff were taken out and a bit of good plain glass put in, it would be easier to find things in the vestry. He is a great soul, really, but glass is not in his line. You see how rich and deep the colouring is, and you will notice the fragment in the top right-hand corner—the one just above the fourteenth-century Madonna. It is the most precious piece of all, and is thought to be thirteenth century. It came from a lancet when the chancel was rebuilt in 1892. Someone threw all the glass away, and it was only by the merest chance that my predecessor saved the fragment you see here.

'But you must see the brass near the altar, a full-length portrait of a fifteenth-century vicar. Whenever I get an American visitor, which isn't often, I take an unchristian delight in telling him that in the whole of his vast continent he has not a brass like this, *or shouldn't have*. Old Peter Roncliffe was ministering here centuries before Washington's day; and you will notice that the brass is peculiar for having an unfinished inscription. The engraver, as you see, began writing a verse about Peter, but never finished it. It was very careless of him, but we will forgive him—he has been dead long enough.'

'It is all very interesting,' I said. 'I had no idea you had so many treasures in your church.'

I do not think he heard what I said. He was striding down the nave. 'See the monument on the left?' he asked. 'It is worth reading; it tells how an entire family, father, mother and four children, died within ten days of each other. The ugly monument above is to old Sir William Templeham who received the estates here as a reward for doing nothing in the seventeenth century. His son signed Charles the First's death warrant. We are far enough from the sea, but on the south wall is an inscription to a sailor who was at sea for fifty days, and died within sight of land. His mother sleeps in the churchyard. It is all rather pathetic and strange, isn't it? I don't want to bore you, but I should like you to see the panels in the reredos. They are thought to be 600 years old, though the framework was made by a local woodcarver. One of the panels is a bit of a mystery. I think it must be intended to show the supper at Emmaus, but what the odd thing on the table is, I have never been able to make out. Oh, and the pulpit is Jacobean, as you will see at a glance. The last vicar but one died in it. He was seventy-three, and had just given out his text 'I go to prepare a place for you.' He had always said he wanted to die in harness, and his wish was realized.

'One other thing,' he said, hurrying me down the aisle to the tower. 'We had to have some repairs done a year ago—and now we are raising money to repair the organ, much to the organ-blower's disgust—and the workmen found a Saxon stone with two very queer figures sitting under arches. They are thought to be unique, and the British Museum has offered me a hundred pounds for them. I think we shall keep them, however, though we could do with the money. It is queer to think these two little chaps have been here all the time, and not one of us the wiser.'

'Yes,' I said. 'But something else interests me—two bigger men are here, and one is much the wiser. You have made the past live.'

'Oh no,' he answered quickly. 'Not a bit of it. The fact is, I've always had a great hope of thoroughly restoring the church—taking down the old plaster partition there, and making the place beautiful, worthy. I'd have the churchwarden windows out, and something lovely, spiritual, in their place, but money . . . money is scarce, and we want to keep our little old men. We are spending over two hundred on renovating the organ, and I shall be glad to have it in a satisfactory condition. It will help to make the service more beautiful and more reverent. I am a great believer in bright services, good singing, short sermons. I see hopes of a spiritual revival. I love the past enshrined in our churches, but it is our business—us parsons, I mean—to look after the present. That is our first job. I am glad to say that with the help of a wonderful woman we are working up the Sunday school . . .'

'Yes,' I said, 'I know her. I stayed at her cottage last night.'

'You did? Isn't she a gracious woman? She helps me to live a bit nearer the man I meant to be. Such simplicity, such faith. You'll know her story?'

'No.'

'Ah, she would not tell you. You see how white her hair is, and yet she is not really old. Her husband—so the story goes—was one of the best men who ever breathed; a musician, and the composer of rare organ music. He had money, too. Then he lost it owing to being embezzled by one he thought his friend. After that the war came. They had one child—and she died before she was two, and early in 1915 her husband went out one night—they were living down Bermondsey way then—and was never seen, or heard of, again.'

'They couldn't trace him at all?'

'No. That's why her hair is white. I think that's why she has that almost childish simplicity. She's the soul of the parish. Every one goes to her for love and guidance and comfort. She darns socks, and gives the money, a half-penny a pair, to the church missionary fund. She's the bravest woman I know.'

As he said this I remembered her words about him—'the bravest man I know.' How deeply ran the river of life in this tranquil village!

We had come out into the sunshine; William was hobbling down the road, I could just see him framed by two trees near the churchyard gate. 'Come and look in at the vicarage,' the vicar said. 'Perhaps you'll stay to lunch? I'd love a talk about things.'

'I've promised to return to Beulah,' I told him. 'Otherwise I would have come like a shot.'

He paused. 'Look here,' he said suddenly, 'we ought to have a chat—at any rate I ought. I rarely get one. I shall be out most of the day, but if you are staying round here why not come to dinner at seven?' Before I could reply he added, 'And by the way, stay the night!'

I looked at his eager face. 'You are very kind,' I said. 'I'm a stranger you know.'

'I'll take the immense risk,' he said. 'Seven then.'

So we parted, and I looked round the village before going in search of a midday meal. I talked with my hostess about the impulsive parson, and heard more of his good deeds. In the afternoon I helped with the gardening, weeding, in spite of many protests from the quiet lady. I also chopped enough firewood to last a couple of months; and I was careful to do all this, mark you, *after* I had paid my reckoning, knowing that had I done it before she would have knocked something off.

When I took my leave she gave me a little brown-paper bag and patted my arm saying, 'You might give him these, he'll want them for Sunday,' and as they were soft and light I presumed they were socks for the ministerial feet—feet which loved to minister—the work of hands that loved to do good. What a beautiful world it is!

It was like calling on an old friend my turning up, so to speak, at the big, rambling vicarage among elms and rhododendrons. Only half the house was lived in, but the dining-room, with its massive Victorian furniture, was solidly comfortable, and after a dinner well served, we went into the vicar's study, a spacious room with many books. There was a log fire smouldering in the grate. 'I always like a bit of fire in the evening,' he explained. 'It's company.' On the marble mantelpiece stood a photograph of a gracious woman. I knew she had been his wife.

Tall, spare, rather whimsical, he charged his pipe while glancing round his books. 'Only half of them read,' he confessed. 'No time for reading. I was a great reader years ago, but a parson hasn't time to vegetate amid theology.'

'I thought that was what they usually did?'

'Some do,' he agreed. 'I try to keep *alive*. The fact is,' he paused to light his pipe, 'I once had a great idea of writing a book. I longed to write it. Indeed, I began it, and wrote twenty thousand words.' He looked up at a shelf. 'It's lying up there,' he remarked, pointing to a brown paper parcel. 'It was a history of the parish. As you may have gathered, this is an exceptionally interesting neighbourhood to the antiquarian and historian. Geologists come here to study the peculiar formation of the strata. Antiquarians have an idea—I entertained the county Archæological Society here only last month—that there was a Roman villa within a hundred yards of this house. We may be sitting near the spot where a Roman dreamed of the yellow Tiber. . .

> And how can man die better
> Than facing fearful odds
> For the ashes of his fathers
> And the temples of his gods?

Great old boy, Macaulay; I worshipped him at school! Then we have, as you observed, traces of Saxon and Norman work in the church; and there is reason to believe we gave England two sea-dogs, a famous poet, a martyr, and a fellow who got himself hanged.'

'Plenty of variety,' I murmured.

'Well, all this I would have worked into my book, together with facts given me by old Sir George—facts relating to six hundred years of the manorial rights.' He spread out his hands. 'But you see, a vicar has to be more than an antiquarian.'

I nodded.

'So I talked it over with my wife—she went through the mists three years ago.' (He said this quite dispassionately, and not a nerve in his face trembled.) 'And we both knew instinctively what to do. So I put the book on the shelf. And there it is to-day—rather dusty.'

'The kingdom of God comes first?'

'Always. It must. You see, that is what the Church so often forgets. My own, shall I say, educated self, longs to restore the old building, as I told you this morning, to make it more beautiful, to preserve its old charm, to spend, say, three thousand pounds on it. But that would mean raising money, having endless committees and meetings. We should all have to put our shoulders to the wheel, and the danger of it is that in going all out for the secondary things, we forget the primary.'

I told him I knew he was right.

He sat back in his chair, smoking in silence. I saw a faint mocking smile at the corners of his lips. 'Years ago,' he said, 'in my earliest twenties, I was a sceptical fellow. I got into the Church by the skin of my teeth. I had a great idea for a terrible book.' He hesitated. 'Do you know,' he said, 'I feel awfully ashamed of myself doing all the talking in this way. Do forgive me.'

'Vicar,' I replied, 'I am smoking your tobacco. I believe—guessing mostly—you devote yourself to others, and rarely give yourself a chance to take an airing. I am on pilgrimage in search of all that is best in men and women. You will do me a signal favour by going on talking in the charming way you have been doing.'

He regarded me with a new interest. 'Well, anyhow,' he said, 'I had the great idea of writing a book in a cynical vein. I'd have it in three parts, I thought. First, a man groping for a faith. He was to be an intellectual giant seeing the wretched and ghastly mistake of Christianity. He was to think his way to a whole new system of religion which was to be intensely spiritual and practical. Remember, I was only twenty-two. So our first part closes with the super-man becoming a devotee of his new religion. Got that?'

'Yes.'

'Well then, part two shows us the miraculous spread of the new cult! It is taken up among the middle classes. It runs through the old country. New societies are formed, a second Ignatius Loyola comes to life. New hymns are composed, new services devised, and new buildings put up everywhere. Can you feel the spread of the movement— its intensity, wonder, force? It goes over the Atlantic, rouses America, and swings round the world in a quarter of a century. And the great high priest is our hero, Mr. Jones.'

'Well?'

He stood up. 'I wrote the first and second parts,' he said, 'eighty thousand words! I let my sarcasm have free rein. And I ended part two with a ghastly scene. I revealed, perhaps you have already sensed it, I revealed the fact that Mr. Jones had lost his faith, had seen through the gaudy tinsel, and had discovered that the whole thing was worthless—an empty delusion! So we were to come to the third part which I never wrote.'

'How was that?'

'I was told not to.'

'Your wife?'

'No. I didn't know her then. I just felt something tell me I was being a renegade to my conscience. I have the two parts up there on the shelf,' he said, glancing up again. 'They are there, those eighty thousand words, and I *know* a dozen publishers would have jumped at a chance to publish the finished work. It was scathing— and clever, too. I re-read it last winter, and I marvelled at it. But you see, I was doing it to smash things, not to build. I was doing it to bring fame to my own shrivelled soul! It was the devil's work—as old William would say. No, it was not sincere. I couldn't go on with it, and when I fell in love with my wife, I couldn't ask her to marry me until I'd told her what I'd nearly done.'

I smiled at that. What an unconscious revelation of himself it was!

'You see,' he went on, 'I began to understand

that it is easier to be a great humbug than to be a little man, and sincere. I saw that it is a finer thing to be a country parson, and do the job nearest to hand, and do it as Christ would have it done, than to stir the world, and beat the big drum. It is easier, at any rate for some of us, to play the first fiddle, but often the second fiddle is best. I'm glad, now, I did not finish the book. It would have made me famous.'

'You are glad it did not make you famous?'

'Very. I'm glad and thankful. God spoke to me, and I understood, and obeyed. He needed me in this corner of England. Yes, you'll think it ridiculous of me to say I could have been famous, but I *know* it. There's a vogue still for the sort of book I nearly wrote. But you see how it would have *separated* me from people? Even as it was, I couldn't get near enough to them. So God was very good. He asked my wife to go and be with Him.'

I said nothing. My pipe had gone out. I sat there in the gentle light, and waited.

There was no huskiness in his voice. He spoke matter-of-factly. One might have thought him callous, had not the rare spirit of the man shone in his face. 'You see,' he said, using his favourite phrase, 'the only thing to draw men very close to each other is suffering and sorrow. It makes you able to understand. It gives you—shall I say, a bit of genius for understanding and sympathizing. It is the dark way that brings you to the light where you begin to see people as Jesus saw them, looking through the surface where the differences are veneered, to the self below where we are all pretty much the same. So my wife suffered, and I suffered in sharing her suffering, and when God called her through the mists that separate this world from the next, I understood His love. He had to sacrifice His Son to get our love; He had to sacrifice my wife to make me what He wanted me to be.'

So there was another silence.

'Sir,' said I, 'you must forgive me for thanking you for bringing me here to-night. You have deepened my faith, and I think you are living a sermon I shall not easily forget.'

He did not reply for a few minutes. We relighted our pipes. Then he rose, kicked the log so that a shower of sparks flew out, and said suddenly, 'Life's a great mystery, but very wonderful. Don't you think so?'

I agreed.

'I've talked enough about myself,' he added. 'But I can tell you an odd story of a man I knew in Hull some years ago. It's often puzzled me, and I recall it now because he and I talked as we are doing here, and the incident has often been with me since my wife passed on. Would you care to hear it?'

'I should.'

'I don't know that it is really worth telling, except as a sort of curiosity. It appeals to me more than to some men because, strangely enough, I do not find it quite so impossible as some people seem to find it. After all, the material and the spiritual are much the same, aren't they?'

'Very much,' I said, thinking of my friend,

Smith, and his scientific universe which was as plain as a pikestaff.

'Still, I confess I cannot really make head or tail of the story, and I tell it only because we are agreed that life is a mystery. It goes back to my Oxford days when I knew a man who was many years older than myself. His family and mine had lived next door to each other for years, and he had a good post with an old-established firm. We were great friends in spite of the fact that he was so much older than I; and when I went to Oxford he used to write me long letters. Sometimes he sent verses, most of them mystical. Yet no man was ever more practical. He had a good business head, and was most capable at figures. He was the last man to see visions and dream dreams.

'Well, one Christmas I spent a night at his house. He had begged me to go, I might almost say, implored me. We talked until the early hours of the morning, and though his wife had died only a few weeks before, he seemed wonderfully cheerful. He told me about the new plans the firm had under consideration, and talked quite cheerfully about the work in hand. Then he knelt down to stir the fire, which had fallen very low, and when he got up again he began talking about dreams, and said how strange they were. He asked me what I thought of them, and I told him I never did. I remember watching him swinging the poker between his knees and staring straight before him. I thought perhaps he was going to talk about his wife, but he said, "It's very strange that I can never overtake the man round the corner."

'Honestly, when he said that it gave me the creeps, but he went on quite normally and said that he had had a very queer experience, or rather a series of queer experiences, the first happening when he was little more than a boy. He told me he would have forgotten it if it had not been for what happened afterwards. He asked me not to laugh at him and went on to say that one evening when he was about seventeen he was on his way home from work, feeling particularly happy because he had had a rise and his prospects were good. He had been debating whether or not to celebrate by buying a book or going to the theatre, and was turning the matter over in his mind as he hurried along the street in broad daylight when he saw a young fellow ahead of him. For some un-accountable reason he felt he must see the young man's face, so he quickened his pace to overtake him. To his surprise the young man hurried on, and though my friend gained on him it was a minute or two before he was level with him. Taking long strides he almost overtook the stranger, and turned to look at his face, but at that moment they came to the street corner, and the young fellow disappeared. He did not go into one of the warehouses or shops or offices. He *vanished*.

'Well, my friend would have forgotten the incident had not something brought it to his mind again. About four years afterwards he was in two minds whether to leave the firm or not. There was a slump in trade and he had a chance, as it appeared, of getting a better post, one he would have jumped at if he had not given one of the

Hh

partners a sort of promise to remain. It was a bitterly cold February night. He was walking down a street on his way to his lodgings—the family had moved out of the city—and was wondering what he should do when, quite suddenly, he looked up and saw the figure again. It was different somehow, older and perhaps a little taller, but he recognized it and could not take his eyes from it as it walked slowly in front of him. He rapidly gained on it, came level with it, and almost grasped its arm, though he had no idea why he wanted to, but they reached the street corner at that moment, and he found himself alone.'

'Very curious,' I said. 'I suppose it could be nothing more than imagination.'

'But the story becomes stranger,' said the vicar. 'My friend did not see the figure again for many years—not until the night before his wedding. I was the best man, but I knew nothing at the time of the odd thing which happened that night. He saw the phantom (I think I must call it by that name) a few hours before he stood at the altar. I had been with him earlier in the evening, leaving him perhaps about ten. About eleven he ran to the pillar-box at the corner of the road, and had just dropped a letter in the box when he was startled by seeing the familiar shape again. It was not a yard from him. Unthinkingly, he darted forward, determined to see its face, but it was too quick for him and vanished instantly.'

'A delusion,' I said. 'It must have been.'

My host nodded. 'Possibly it was,' he said. 'Yes, it may have been. But listen. I tell you,

sitting there that night and listening to him, I
felt there was a meaning somewhere. You see, he
saw this thing, whatever it was, several times after
that. He saw it once when he was worried about
his mother. He saw it the night his daughter died.
She was only three. He said the figure seemed to
stoop, and he ran forward to see it, and though it
vanished at the corner, there was something very
peculiar that time—it was humming softly.'

'But that might have been imagination, too,' I
pointed out.

'Yes, it might. Well, then, he saw it again the
day after his wife's funeral. I shall never forget
how he spoke about it, sitting by the fire, swinging
the poker, and telling me very tragically how, on
the afternoon of that day—it was in November—
he had walked up to the cemetery to look at the
grave again. He had come home through a fog,
and suddenly the figure was walking before him.
He was seized with an overwhelming desire to way-
lay it, and made a frantic rush to take it by the
arm. He had almost laid hands on it when they
came to a corner, and the shape disappeared; but
he told me that he was sure it was singing. I
remember how he held the poker erect—funny
how we remember these little things, isn't it? He
looked an old man. Suddenly he turned to me,
and said, "I shall see him again. I know I shall,
and what I can't understand is why, up to now,
I've never thought of shouting out to him to stop.
I will shout to him to stop the next time I see
him."'

The vicar was silent.

'Did he see him again?' I asked.

'I don't know,' he replied. 'I rather think so. You see, the whole story is strange, but the strangest thing of all is that less than three weeks after that talk he was killed at the corner of the road he lived in, knocked down by a taxi. At the inquest the driver said he had been driving along the road at a normal speed when a man suddenly dashed from the pavement shouting, "Stop! Stop!" He added that the man ran straight in front of him, without looking either to the right or left, and that although he jammed his brakes on, he was over him before he could pull up. That is how he died.'

'It is certainly very strange,' I said.

'I think so,' the vicar replied. 'And the oddest thing is the witness of the taxi-driver who declared that there wasn't another soul in sight.'

'And what do you make of it?' I asked.

He shrugged his shoulders. 'I don't know. Sometimes nothing. Sometimes—oh, well, it's late. Perhaps it is another proof that the world has more mystery in it than we care to admit. You see, life is stranger than any of us know. We are spirit as well as flesh and blood. I do not find the story hard to believe, because much of my life is directed by what seem to be outside influences.'

Presently he held a lamp for me to see my way upstairs—for, as he said humorously, 'though we have the electric wires in the house, and the bulbs waiting to be put into all the rooms, we lack the power from afar. Given that, we shall see.'

'And understand,' said I turning to the landing.

So I went to bed in a large room. My mind was

too active for sleep. That queer story bothered me. This great man, doing a little good magnificently, amazed me. In this mood I took out Thomas from my jacket pocket (my jacket hanging handily at the bed foot) and by the soft lamplight I opened it at the page where he wisely says:

'Be not, therefore, elated in thine own mind because of any art or science, but rather let the knowledge given thee make thee afraid. If thou thinkest thou understandest and knowest much, *know that there be many more things that thou knowest not*.'

Well, that was written long ago, but it is true to-day. I turned out the lamp, and lay in the darkness, so great a darkness that I could see nothing. The curtains were drawn across the window, but presently I grew accustomed to the blackness, and saw a blue wedge between the curtains, and in the wedge a solitary star. Then I fell asleep.

CHAPTER V

I pray in church; take leave of a lady with white hair; have a distant view of semi-detached legs; read Stevenson aloud on a hill; walk ten miles with a boy who loved stars, and birds, and flowers, and things; ride into a thunder-storm; meet a man from Africa; find 'a queer bird' playing patience; have a word or two with a poetical Boots; and astonish a man who was nearly forty.

WE HAD BREAKFASTED, talked about the Gospel of St. John, discussed Stevenson's *Virginibus*, argued about the Yellow Peril, agreed on the tendency in modern fiction, and devised a new system of distributing garden produce and small fruits to the benefit of every one—all by 8.15 the next morning. Then we went to the church. The door was locked, for old William had not reached it with his key; and kneeling down we said a prayer. When I dropped something into the box for 'Organ Renovation', the vicar said I ought not to have done anything of the sort, so we parted at cross-purposes, but smiling; and if ever I go that way again I am under a solemn obligation to spend another night at the vicarage.

I looked in to see the lady with white hair. She gave me a smile which was a blessing and a benediction, and inquired if I thought my socks needed to be mended. I assured her they were not then in need of repair. As I passed through the village I caught sight of William's 'semi-detached' legs in the distance, and though I did not go back to

renew my acquaintance with the owner, I thought
that he had been right, and that, after all, Providence *had* directed me to him.

I was on my way a little after nine by the church
clock. There was sunshine on my path but I saw
heavy clouds on the horizon, and felt a change of
weather brewing. Not, indeed, that my prognos-
tication was worth paying much attention to, for
I am notoriously incapable of prophesying the kind
of day we are to have, and am little versed in those
outdoor signs of cloud and sun and a thousand
other ways by which country folk foretell to-
morrow's weather. For them, I suppose, cows
lying down indicate a fine day; a 'mackerel' sky
tells them that wind is coming; gnats dancing in
the evening sunshine are a clear proof that we are
to have a spell of dry weather. It is all very wonderful, but I leave these forms of divination to the
necromancers of the open air, and am content to
take the day's weather as it comes, for come it
will, wet or fine. Besides, it is the weather a man
carries about with him that matters most.

The way was uphill a little, and coming to the
highest point I stood still awhile to look over the
countryside. Very fair it was to look over, for I
doubt if anywhere in the wide world you will find
pastoral scenery to equal some of our English
countryside, particularly when one is approaching
the heart of our island where little hills and
spacious fields, and a thousand shades of green
stretch away into a blue haze, with here and there
a streak of silver, a splash of buttercup-gold, a
cluster of red roofs, a grey spire, a white ribbon of

road, and all the abiding fairness of a land for which men have died with a cheer. All this I saw from the little hilltop where the wind was pleasant; nevertheless there was a hint of smoke under the clouds in the distance, and at the farther end of the valley were the outlines of pit-heads. I knew my day's journey must bring me out of rural into industrial England, and I knew that between those sombre clouds and the last green rise a dozen miles ahead were crowded colliery areas.

I was in no hurry to reach them. I stood in the middle of the road and took out *Virginibus*, and read it in the open air, a very pleasant thing to do. I read aloud, for good English has its own music and is pleasant to hear. So, for the sheer joy of it, I began with that paragraph, 'O unwearied feet travelling ye know not whither . . .' Well, my feet were unwearied then—and there were no holes in my socks. Presently, turning back a page, I read:

'Happily we all shoot at the moon with ineffectual arrows; our hopes are set on an inaccessible El Dorado; we come to an end of nothing here below. Interests are only plucked up to sow themselves again like mustard. You would think, when the child was born, there would be an end to trouble; and yet it is only the beginning of fresh anxieties; and when you have seen it through its teething and its education, and at last its marriage, alas! it is only to have new fears, new quivering sensibilities, with every day; and the health of your children's children grows as touching a concern as that of your own. Again, when you have married your wife, you would think you were got upon a hilltop, and might begin to go downward by an easy slope. But you have only ended courting to begin marriage. Falling in love and winning love are often difficult tasks to overbearing and rebellious spirits; but to keep in love is also a business of some importance, to which both man and wife must bring kindness and goodwill. The true love story commences at the altar, when there lies before the married pair a most beautiful contest of wisdom and generosity, and a life-long struggle towards an unattainable ideal.'

Now, if you will open your *Virginibus*, you will see at once that there is another line and a half of the paragraph, but this I did not recite, for I became aware that I was not alone. Reading Stevenson aloud on a hilltop before ten in the morning is a very fine thing, but reading aloud to an audience on a hill before ten in the morning is a pastime which may possibly require a little explanation. I do not know that any of our statesmen or politicians have cultivated the habit of reading aloud on hilltops before ten in the morning, probably owing to the difficulty of reaching a suitable hill so early. At any rate, it is not, shall we say, an established custom of the English people. This being so, I stopped short and looked at the small, rather freckled, boy who was regarding me with genuine astonishment. 'Good morning!' I said. 'You needn't be scared, my boy. I am learning to read aloud!'

'I wasn't scared,' he retorted. 'I was just wondering.'

'Oh? Wondering? About me?'

'Yes. I was wondering why you did it.'

'The reading? Well now, that is easily explained. You see, I have a book here by a man you'll have heard of, and a capital man he was, too. He wrote *Treasure Island.*'

'You mean Robert Louis Stevenson?'

'You are an intelligent boy. Yes, I mean Stevenson who was a lover of the out-of-doors, and was a traveller, and a very brave man . . .'

'I thought he only wrote books.'

'No. He did more than that. He suffered a lot. He had many things to make him miserable, but he kept cheerful and smiling. That was brave, wasn't it?'

He nodded. 'That's like my Mum,' he said. 'She's brave. She smiles when she feels like crying. I help her with the work sometimes, but I'm having a day off to-day.'

'Oh? You're not at school to-day then?'

'No. Our school has a holiday to-day. I'm glad. I told my mother I would stay and help her, but she said I was to go off a bit.'

He was a delightful little fellow—about eleven or twelve. He had curly hair, and a frank, smiling face, with serious eyes. He was a bit old-fashioned; life seemed to have taught him more than he ought to have known. His clothes were neat, but his jacket was patched, and I guessed there was not too much money to spend at their house. He had a tin box and a pocketful of match-boxes, and there was a little book sticking out of another pocket.

'You are a naturalist?' I asked.

He flushed. 'Oh, no,' he said. 'Not properly.

But I like birds, and flowers, and stars, and things.'

'Then you *are* a naturalist,' I said. 'I'm a bit of a naturalist, too. I love hedges and birds. Isn't it wonderful how a blackbird lines its nest with mud, and makes it all so smooth and round? And I remember once, when I was a boy, I went down by a river and watched a water vole come out to look at me, and I kept so very still it actually sat on my shoe . . .'

His shyness was leaving him. His eyes sparkled. 'Did you, really?' he inquired eagerly. 'That's topping. I've never had one do that. I guess I can't keep still long enough. I've got a queer sort of moth in one of my match-boxes, but I'm looking for a death's head. They're scarce, you know. I know a lot of wild flowers, too. I like them.'

'How do you recognize them?'

'Oh, I've a book about them. Mum bought it at a jumble sale.' He was tugging at his pocket, and out came a very old book with frightful illustrations. 'Sometimes I take some of the flowers home and draw them on the bits of paper we have. I've made a list of all the plants I've found round about. I've got over a hundred.'

'Splendid,' I said. 'I used to do something like that when I was a boy—but I never got anywhere near a hundred. I should think your father and mother are proud of you.'

'Mother likes me doing it all,' he said.

'But not your father?'

'Not much. He says it's a waste of time. He likes practical people. He's a practical man when he has any work, but he's been out a long time, as long as I can remember. We have lodgers, but he doesn't help much with them. I ought not to come away to-day, but Mum made me. Some day I'm going to do a big thing.'

'Oh? What is that?'

He paused. 'You see the river?' he asked, pointing down the valley. 'Well, some day I want to find where it begins. I've always wanted to.'

'It must be a long way from here,' I said.

He nodded. 'Yes, I 'spects it is. But I'll explore it some day. I know a path along it. That's where I'm going now.'

'May I come with you?'

'Would you really like?'

'Of course I should. You will be able to tell me things.'

'Oh, I don't know about that. I don't know much, really. But I like everything alive. I like stars, too. I have a half-crown telescope I saved up for, for my birthday. I can't make up my mind whether to be an astronomer or a botanist, or what father says.'

'What does he say?'

'He says insurance is a paying game.'

'And your mother?'

His eyes lighted up. 'Oh,' he said, 'she doesn't mind. She wants me to be something good. She'd come botanizing with me if she could.'

'She hasn't time?'

'No. We have lodgers. I help to clean the knives.'

So we went down the hill, and climbed a stile,

and followed a path by the river, and very pleasant it was, with meadows at one side, and willows and ash-trees at the other; and there was much to see, and hear, and feel. We found a lark's nest, and a thrush with a wounded wing which my young friend promptly tried to bind up with a bit of my handkerchief. By good fortune I found a bar of chocolate in my haversack, and we made short work of it. We saw the silver on the river turn to grey, and a dark shadow ruffle up against the flow, and we knew thunder was in the air. But we went on, for the river brought us nearer a small market-town where my companion could get a 'bus home. We scared a pheasant, gathered some flowers, and talked about perpetual motion, and Galileo, and how to make an aquarium, and whether it was ever true that salamanders could live in fire; and so the hours tripped by, and it was half-past three on a cloudy afternoon when we decided that it was no use trying to reach the head of the river. 'It goes on and on,' I said as we came to another bend.

We stood still. The market-town was half a mile away. We could see the cars and 'buses passing over the single-arch bridge. Beyond were houses by the water, and farther still another sweep of the river under trees. We lost it there. 'It goes a long way,' he said, rather wistfully I thought.

'Yes,' I said. 'It would take several days' walking to get up among the hills where it rises.'

'I didn't think it was quite so far,' he admitted. 'I guess it will be a bit before I find the beginning. I wanted to. I wanted to be the only boy in our class who had ever reached it.'

'Don't worry,' I said. 'You've made a jolly good shot. You must be tired. I should think we've walked ten miles to-day. It's a long way, and I've enjoyed it.'

He looked up at me with a new interest. 'Have you?' he asked. 'I didn't think you would think much of being with me.'

'That's where you're wrong,' I said. 'I've enjoyed every minute of it. Besides, you've taught me lots of things.'

There was a quick glance. 'You don't mean that,' he said. 'You mean you've taught me heaps. All about the way they cook elephant's foot, and about counting the rings on a tree, and all that.'

'No,' I said seriously. 'I mean what I say. You've taught me a lot. You won't understand how.' I paused. Then I said, 'Come along, old man. You've got to get back home, or the police will be looking for you. Come on!'

We took a short cut across a meadow, and came into the sleepy market-town where we found a teashop. In we went, and I ordered ham sand-wiches and tea, and cakes. We had an ice-cream, and I bought a dozen buns and had them put in a carrier, and one was a special one with chocolate on the top, and that was for the naturalist's mother. Then we hunted out a stationer, and though he had not the book I wanted, he had two books about natural history, one about trees, and one about birds and their nests. I bought them for the naturalist, and saw him flush, and watched him fight a battle, trying to say he wouldn't take them, and giving in in the end. 'I'd rather not,' he declared faint-heartedly, his eyes nearly jumping out of his head when he saw the illustrations.

'Come on,' I said, 'to please me!'

That crushed him. He took them.

We went to the 'bus station, and had ten minutes to wait. He kept looking in his books. 'My,' he exclaimed, 'I'll be a naturalist now. The other fellows in my class won't half stare. It's been a great day, hasn't it?'

'A great day,' I said.

Then the 'bus came in. I paid his fare, and pushed half-a-crown into his hand. 'Good-bye, laddie,' I said. 'Keep on loving flowers, and stars, and birds, and things. Even if you have to be an insurance agent, keep on loving them. And God be with you.' Then we shook hands much as Livingstone and Stanley did when they met in Darkest Africa.

There was a 'bus for the mining town six or seven miles away. I considered it. True, I was on a walking tour, but there seemed little point in trudging along dreary miles of road. I heard a distant rumble of thunder, and straightway climbed into the 'bus. My companion who had been so young and fresh was a much more splendid pilgrim than I. If we two could have gone on day after day like that, how fine it would have been! I realized that it was his youth which was making me feel old.

By this time we had left the sleepy little town and were driving towards a thunder-storm. 'Looks bad, eh?' the conductor remarked when he came for my fare. 'I knew we should have it before the day was out.'

I agreed, and sank back into my thoughts. We were leaving the fields. I caught a glimpse of the river, sullen and slate-colour under the threatening sky. We passed a dismantled pit-head, a derelict place which spoiled everything. We ran through a poor village with about six streets of brick houses, all alike. We came to a tumble-down factory without an unbroken pane of glass in its windows. We passed a long row of hoardings hiding the distant hills, the advertisements for somebody's beer, and somebody's soap, and somebody's something else, and I began to wonder if my pilgrimage were ended. We invaded a territory given over completely to wire netting and chicken houses. We passed a cement chapel where saints alone could worship God. We jolted over several railway crossings, and came to a grey land of chimneys and smoke, and slag heaps, desolate and dreary. There were men without collars, most of them standing about outside public-houses, some reading sporting papers, one or two with greyhounds on leashes. There were stacks of coal in railway sidings. We left the macadam road for sets, and the 'bus jolted over another level crossing, swung round a public-house, and came to a standstill in a square with a War Memorial which had a soldier on a pedestal, and an inscription that said, 'To the glorious dead.' I thought the dead were better off than many of the living round about.

I heard a deep roll of thunder and decided to take shelter at the hotel facing the square. The hall porter eyed me rather doubtfully, and I dare say I cut an odd figure—my dusty jacket and shoes, my haversack, my hair disarranged, my face brown and perhaps none too clean. I was shown to a bedroom where I could look into the square. Presently I went in search of dinner, securing a table by a window so that I could watch the lightning which had already begun to play over the roofs, great purple ribbons running over half the sky. I think the food was good, but my attention was on the storm outside. There was little rain, and the spectacle of the lightning shattering the clouds was magnificent. I think there would be a dozen of us in the room, but sometimes the murmur of conversation would cease as every one looked up when a particularly vivid flash glittered about us, followed immediately by a bombardment from the heavy artillery of heaven.

Towards the end of the meal a man at the table next to mine put down his paper and turned to catch my eye. 'What do you think of *that*?' he asked, referring to a deafening cannonade.

'Pretty bad,' I replied.

He was a thick-set man, not very attractive. 'I've travelled a goodish bit,' he said, 'but I haven't heard much—see that? I haven't—Lord above, that must mean a thunderbolt! Pity they can't muffle it a bit, eh? I've been in African thunderstorms, get 'em bad out there at some seasons I can tell you. I never did like thunder. There it is again—see it? Right over the church? Now for it!' He ducked, as if to miss the force of the thunder.

Iн

'Yes,' I said. 'I know they have them round Bloemfontein.'

He had turned to finish his biscuits and cheese, but he looked round quickly. 'Eh, Bloemfontein? Been there?'

I shook my head. 'No, I said, but I know a bit about it. A friend of mine is out there still.'

'Not in the line of steel-casting by any chance?'

I smiled. 'No,' I said. 'He's in the newspaper line. Went out to Bloemfontein six years ago, or more.'

'Newspaper? Indeed. I shouldn't know him then. I've always been in the steel trade myself, though I sold my old house to a chap on the *South African Reporter*. Decent chap. I only saw him once, when we fixed things up. Name was White.'

'White?' I repeated in surprise. 'Not Joseph White?'

He nipped his thick lips with a stumpy thumb and finger. 'Couldn't say for sure,' he said. 'I've an idea it was J. White, but I'm not sure. There's a crash for you. That means damage somewhere, I guess. Tall chap, he was, if I remember rightly. It's six or seven years since now. Had his wife in England, and said he'd get her out there if he got a house . . .'

I had been fumbling in my wallet. I opened a letter, and read out the address at the top. He started. 'Good Lord,' he said, 'that's the one; that's my old address. I lived there eight years.' Then, as the coincidence was borne in on his mind, 'Well, now, isn't that odd? To think the world's such a little place. I often wondered how he got along. He seemed a decent chap. And you know him?'

'Very well. I haven't seen him since he went out there, about six years ago, as you say. He has two children, and is doing well. Strange he should live in your house!'

'My hat, that's a flash!' he exclaimed. 'Hanged if I like lightning, and I've to go. I have to catch a train in a few minutes.' He handed me his card. 'I live near Windsor,' he said laconically. 'No relation to the King, you know. I'd be delighted to see you sometime. Funny thing how we've met, isn't it? Wish I'd been staying the night. We'd had a talk. Strange we should meet, eh? If you read it in a book you'd say it was far-fetched, I guess? Funny thing, life, isn't it?'

Then we shook hands, and he went. From the window I saw him crossing the square to the station. I have lost his card, and doubt if I shall ever see him again. But I shall remember our chance acquaintance.

'Funny thing, life,' that was how he put it. I suppose he was right, though 'funny' is hardly the word I should use. A mysterious thing, certainly. That is one of the glories of it. You never know what is round the corner. If it is good, then it is a surprise; if ill, then the possibility of it helps us to value the good while we have it. There is no boredom. You meet one man, and he is eaten up by caterpillars—I mean, all his talk is about the caterpillars of the white butterfly which destroy his cabbages. You meet another, and he has a remedy for all our ills; another, and he looks simple, and is wise; another is an authority on beetles; another has a trick of button-holing you, and saying, 'Now look here, let me tell you something for your good'; another is bubbling over with good spirits; another has a grudge against everyone. Meeting someone is always an adventure.

The thunder rumbled into the distance, the rain came down from a leaden sky, and there was no thought of going out. I wandered into the smoke-room where a massive gentleman, who reminded me of Mussolini, had just finished playing a game of patience and was watching the rain while dexterously shuffling two packs of cards.

'Wet,' said the massive man.

'Very,' said I.

The other side of the conversation dealt out his cards with praiseworthy exactitude, and proceeded to play the game with as much concentration as if the fortunes of Europe depended upon the result. Presently the last card was turned face upwards, and the massive man ran a practised eye over the 'set,' gently caressing the lower of his two chins. I turned from the window and remarked (rather impertinently, I admit), 'I'm afraid it will not come out.'

He did not trouble to look up, but said thoughtfully, 'It will not, sir, but you should not be afraid, you should be glad.'

'Indeed?' I asked. 'Surely you play the game hoping to get a clear run.'

The massive man gathered up his cards carefully. 'No,' said he, 'if the game comes out I succeed, and at once lose all interest in it. If it does not come out, I have the joy of trying again. That is where my *patience* comes in. The idea is not to come out, but to stay in, and keep trying to come out.'

Then he dealt the cards again, and attended to his problem with such gravity that I had not the courage to disturb him.

The only other occupant of the smoke-room was a man who appeared to be sound asleep, so I drifted into the lounge and across the hall till I came to a door marked Private, and as it was half open, and as I am what I am, I trespassed along a passage and came to a glass annexe where a pale youth was scraping potatoes. 'The day's work not over yet?' I asked.

'Not yet, sir,' said he, apparently surprised to see me there.

'Do you like potatoes?' I inquired.

'Hate them,' he replied fervently.

'You peel so many?'

He nodded. 'Potatoes and boots,' he said. 'Always potatoes and boots, except when it's boots and potatoes. I dream of them. I see millions of them. And sometimes I see potatoes with sad eyes lying in rows, mile after mile, mile after mile, and I see myself with my feet in immense boots, treading on them and mashing them into pulp. I'd love to do it!'

'A most remarkable dream,' I said.

'Oh, that's nothing,' he replied. 'I dream no end of things, 'specially when there's been something hot for supper.'

I laughed. 'Evidently you have a vivid imagination, which cannot be said of all our modern poets,' I said. I had spoken thoughtlessly, but I stopped short, for his red hands were resting on the rim of the enamel bowl, and he was staring through the glass partition. It was curious to see how rigid he had become, and when I followed his gaze I was surprised that he should stare so long at a dull, brick wall. I half expected him to tell me something about himself, and was a little disappointed when, though he had flushed, he merely remarked, 'It isn't half raining, is it?'

I returned to the hall where the porter was standing with his hands behind him. 'Anything I can do for you, sir?' he asked.

'Arrange for fine weather in the morning,' I said.

'Very good, sir, I'll see the management about it. We don't usually have so much water at once. I don't remember a storm like this for years.'

'You have been here a good while?'

'Over thirty years, sir.'

'That's a long time.'

'Yes, sir. I've seen a few people come and go.'

'And how do you find most of them? Easy to get on with or not?'

'Oh, mostly very fair. A few twisters and disagreeable people come along, of course, but most are very easy to get on with. That's my experience.'

'Do you know what I think all that goes to show?'

'No, sir.'

'I think it goes to show that *you* are easy to get on with. By the way, Boots seems a queer specimen of humanity. I hear he has astonishing dreams.'

He laughed. 'Oh, so he's been talking about his dreams, has he?' he asked. 'He often does that. Poor chap, he's a rum customer. His father was killed in the mine. Boots once had ideas about being poet laureate, but he can't spell. I'm afraid there's something wrong inside him. It's a pity. He keeps on here for his mother's sake, and he often tells me about his dreams. I reckon he won't live so very long.'

He went off in response to a ring, and I strolled back to the smoke-room where I lounged in a chair, wondering how long the massive gentleman would play patience, and how long the other man would sleep. It was not long before the massive gentleman finished a game, gathered up his cards, packed them inside a small leather wallet, and said, 'Good night.'

I said, 'Good night,' and was surprised to hear the other man say, 'Good night,' also. Apparently he had not been asleep, for he opened one eye, looked at me, and remarked, 'Queer bird. In a big way in timber. He and I meet here four times a year, and have done for nearly twenty years. We don't know each other yet! I was amused to hear you speak to him that first time. He said more to you in ten minutes than he has said to me in twice as many years, except the "Good night." Ask how business is with him, and he shuts up like an oyster. Queer bird, very.'

'I see. So you've been coming here year after year for nearly twenty years?'

He sighed. 'That's so, but you needn't remind me of it. I don't care to remember I'm nearly forty.'

'Oh? Is that a catastrophe?'

'Almost! It is the dangerous age. When a man gets to be forty he is in danger of settling down, becoming too comfortable and satisfied. You know what I mean . . .'

'Yes,' I said. 'I know. You are right, it is a very dangerous age. I am with you.' I sighed, and looked sadly at my pipe.

'Mind you,' said he, 'I'm not quite forty yet—but not far off.'

'What's a year or two?' I asked in a depressed voice. 'I had a neighbour, a fine fellow, about your build. He was forty, and a very decent fellow. He was talking with me—as cheerful as you are—one day. He'd gone the next.'

The man in the arm-chair took his feet off the sofa, and sat up. 'Don't misunderstand me,' he said, 'I don't mean that forty is physically dangerous. There's nothing wrong with me.'

'That's what he said,' I remarked. 'You never saw a man with more life and "go" in him.'

'Still, he must have suffered from some complaint, you know . . . to go like that.'

'He was just turned forty,' I reminded him.

'But I don't see that that had anything to do with it,' he began.

'It hadn't,' I agreed. 'He just took it into his head to go, that was all. He never thought he would get it, but then, a man of his age never does entertain high hopes.'

'Get what?'

'The post.'

'I thought you meant he died.'

'Died?' I regarded him seriously, at least I meant to, but I think he saw me smile. 'Bless you,' I said, 'he didn't die. He went off to Australia—had a government appointment.'

He had stood up by now—a fine-looking man, though rather too corpulent. 'Look here,' he said, 'you've been having me on. Anyhow, I'll forgive you. I expect I *do* grouse a bit about being forty. The fact is, I am afraid of growing stale. Life doesn't seem as interesting, as adventurous now as it used to.'

'You carry your trouble before you,' I said.

He looked at his waistcoat, and shook his head sadly.

'Do you do much skipping?' I inquired. 'It is good for the liver, and for your views on philosophy. After all, you are right about forty being the dangerous age. It is, particularly if we allow ourselves to get into a rut—a fairly large one in your case—and if we get into the habit of sitting when we might walk, and sleeping when we might talk . . .'

'I was only dozing.'

'And doing the most dangerous thing of all.'

'What is that?'

'Thinking too much about ourselves. That is very bad for us. If you go on dwelling on the fact that you are almost forty, you will be seventy in six months. Bless you, what if you *are* forty? Is it not the best time of life? You are young enough to do everything a man can want to do, and old enough to have a glimmer of wisdom. It is the age when a man wields power most successfully. Good heavens, man, you ought to skip every morning, climb trees every day, throw your arms round your wife every time you see her, walk about on your toes, and think about the merriest things in the world.'

He looked down at me. For a moment I thought he was going to be offended, for I knew well enough I had no right to begin lecturing him. 'Do you know,' he said frankly, 'you are telling me just what my wife said last week.'

Then I jumped up. I held out my hand. 'Sir,' said I, 'whether you are forty or ninety, you are a lucky chap. If your wife thinks as I do, she is the most sensible woman alive! Go home and tell her so, and act on her advice. How you come to be lucky enough to be her husband beats me. Good night!' Then, having shaken his hand vigorously, I went up to bed, leaving him standing aghast.

CHAPTER VI

I look round a mining town and dislike it; find unexpected beauty; discover heroism among slag heaps; hear about a miner with a great soul; am told there is a difference between knowing Jesus and knowing about Him; strike an uninteresting mile or two of road; ride behind a horse and listen to some comical tales; arrive at a peaceful house; learn the secret of a happy married life; go to bed by candle-light; write about two lovers in a lane; and read Thomas à Kempis after midnight.

It was a clean, fresh world into which I walked soon after eight o'clock the next morning. I had ordered an early breakfast, and after making it my business to have a special word with Boots, I had a chat with the hall porter, and left the hotel without seeing my friend of nearly forty.

The streets were dry, though there were still pools in the gutters, and the steam rose like sad wraiths from the slag heaps. Men were setting up stalls in the square, for it was market-day, and there was quite a bustle in the principal streets. Nevertheless, I felt a sense of depression. Life did not seem to flow as smoothly nor as deeply here. Two charwomen were washing the steps of a cinema, and the poster outside had a lurid scene from the night-life of New York. Looking at it were two young men with thin faces; and as I passed, one turned to the other and said something in a low voice, and winked. I wondered vaguely if either of them was 'walking-out' with a girl. Somehow, I hoped not.

A man in a green apron was polishing the brass-work on a public-house door. He nodded to an elderly man in old slippers. 'Morning, Charlie,' he said.

'Morning,' said the shuffler in a flat voice.

I wondered how much of the shuffler's money had clinked into the till of the 'Cosy Corner.'

I found my way into a street where cats abounded, and where slatternly women were talking in loud voices. I thought of the lady of 'Beulah Cottage,' her neat dress, fair face, white hair, quiet ways, gentle spirit, and refinement. A few unemployed men were looking over the bridge. One or two were studying newspapers. There was a colliery where men were working, and an un-employment bureau where, even at that hour, a score of men were lounging about, doing nothing. 'God made the country,' I thought, 'man made the town.'

Then I turned a corner and came to a bit of heaven.

There was a great slag heap, grey and drab, overtopping a long row of dull brick houses. Beyond was a blaze of living colour, an oasis in a wilderness of cinders, a charming spot with wind-ing paths among flower-beds. There were terraces, lawns, a lily pool, trees (young as yet, but full of promise), a variegated privet hedge, a great mass of glowing geraniums, tunnels under rambler roses soon to be red and white with abundant beauty. There were little alcoves in shady corners amid yew hedges. There was fragrance, loveli-ness, peace.

I had a word with one of the gardeners. 'You have made the wilderness blossom as the rose,' I said.

'We have,' said he with emphasis. 'It was a wretched spot ten years ago. It's only just getting into its stride.'

'It belongs to the town, I suppose?'

'Partly. We bought it ourselves. We had a miners' committee, and the council gave us the land, and said we could go and do our best with it. I reckon they didn't think we'd do much. The rest came out of voluntary subscriptions. We gave ourselves a park, and we keep it going. You'll be a stranger? I thought so. Well, you must go round them trees at the top of the bank, and you'll find a playground for the kiddies, and pitches for cricket, and a pond for sailing model yachts.'

'I see you are proud of it all,' I said.

'Yes, and I've reason to be. It's not every mining town that has a place like this. There was a government chap came down some years ago, and said we'd never get some of the plants to grow —too many chemicals in the air from Warton's factory over yonder,' he motioned with his arm. 'But I'd worked on more than one gentleman's estate before I took to mining in the pit—that's why I got this here job when it was going—and I told him we didn't know half his theories, but we knew how to make things grow, and we'd make them, and we have done. There's London planes growing by the fountain there—they'll be a fine sight fifty years after I'm dust; and if you go to the children's pond you'll see a score of walnut-trees.

I planted them myself. They laughed at me —the authorities. "No, Ben," they said, "it's no use. They'll be dead in no time." "Gentlemen," I said, "we'll see." You can go and see for yourself. This here place is bad enough to live in, I can tell you; but it's not so bad that you can't get God's flowers and trees to grow if you treat 'em gentle.'

'You were a miner?'

'Had to be.'

'And now a gardener?'

'That's so, mister, and let me tell you that even miners like beautiful things.'

I went to look at the playing fields and the yachting pool he had mentioned. Then I took the path to the far gate. Near the gate was a pedestal with a bronze medallion to the honour and memory of three men who had gone down the pit after an explosion, had tried to rescue their friends, and had perished in the attempt. So these miners had courage and chivalry—and loved beauty, too.

The simple monument reminded me of the War Memorial in the square. I thought I would go back to look at it; so back I went to walk slowly round the great stone base. 'Their name liveth for evermore,' I read. There were two hundred names.

I passed the hotel, and went along a busy street. The town was wide awake and the market in full swing. 'Two hundred men,' I thought, 'and this is only a small colliery town.' Two hundred men, all heroes. It was hardly a heroic-looking place.

Across the road was an iron building, a little chapel of the Nonconformists. I read the name of the preacher for the next day. His subject was, 'Making the Best of It.' I wondered if he would have twenty in his congregation. If there were a few, the few must be brave, earnest souls. Any one might go regularly to a well-attended church—the singing and fellowship might be inspirations in themselves. But to go to that wretched little place . . . it would take some grace. 'Was you wanting to look inside, mister?' said a red-haired, stoutish man with a basket in his hand.

'No,' I said. 'Not particularly. I was just reading the subject of to-morrow's sermon.'

'Aye, well, there's no harm done in that. You must forgive me being familiar, like, but I'm one of the congregation. There aren't many more, and I thought happen you was wanting the keys. Joe Crawshaw has 'em, and he lives nobbut across road.'

'Thanks,' I said, 'don't trouble to get them. It's kind of you, though. I suppose you find congregations less to-day than formerly?'

'We do that. I remember that there chapel being built. I was there at the opening service. We used to have a full church every Sunday night in them days—but then, there weren't no football nor cricket of a Sunday. Folk had times for work and play, and worship then. I don't know what we're coming to. Still, a few of us keeps on. The old pastor's no good—past it, and the harmonium is done, and when Mrs. Barret isn't there the singing's like a funeral. But some of us keeps on, you know, biding our time. There'll be a revival at last—in the Lord's good time. And in that day

He'll look to a few of us to be ready at hand. So we just go on.'

'I see. By the way, who is the preacher to-morrow—I notice it's a Mr. Anderson, not a reverend.'

'Oh, he's a young miner. He lives down Vine Street, second on your left. He sometimes comes and gives us a hand when we're hard up—the pastor's too doddery to come to-morrow. He's a fine young chap. Taught himself to read his Greek Testament, and has some ideas of his own, too. Believes in the League of Nations, and isn't frightened of saying so. A lot of hooligans waylaid him coming from a service one night, and ducked him in the yacht pool. A bit after, one of 'em was up for breaking a shop window, and had to pay up, but he hadn't any money (half the pits is closed), so young Mr. Anderson comes along, and pays half the fine for him. It was a right decent thing to do, and nobody would have known who'd done it if it hadn't leaked out. It's not all bread and dripping being a Christian in these days, but that young chap isn't afraid.'

We had been walking on while he was speaking. 'I'm just going to feed the hens,' he said. 'Times are pretty hard just now, as I said, and a few eggs come in handy, though the hens always lay best when eggs is cheapest. However, it can't be helped. We've to make the best on it, as my missus always says. It's the Lord's doing, and that's all there is to it.'

When we came to the lane which led to his hen-run, we parted, though not before my chance acquaintance had said, 'The young chap who is preaching to-morrow gave us a fine sermon last time. He said there was a deal of difference between knowing about Christ, and knowing Him.'

My way was over a level crossing and by a dismantled pit-head. I was soon climbing a hill, and when I reached the top I paused to look back over the valley with its chimneys and slag heaps, and over the town with its unloveliness, and its hidden heroism and grace. 'Knowing Christ and knowing about Him,' I thought. Then I took out Thomas à Kempis, and read:

'When Jesus is present, all is well, and nothing seems difficult; but when Jesus is not present, everything is hard. When Jesus speaks not inwardly to us, all other comfort is nothing worth; but if Jesus speak but one word, we feel great consolation. Did not Mary rise immediately from the place where she wept when Martha said to her, "The Master is come, and calleth for thee"? Happy hour! when Jesus calleth from tears to spiritual joy. Be devout and quiet and Jesus will stay with thee. Love all for Jesus, but Jesus for Himself. For Him, and in Him, let friends as well as foes be dear unto thee; and all these are to be prayed for, that He would make them all to know and to love Him.'

Saul knew about Christ, and persecuted Him. Paul knew Him and served Him. Many of us know about Him, and do Him lip-service. How many of us *know* Him intimately?

Thus I took the echo of that good man's parting

Kн

word, and turned it over in my mind, and used it to help me down the hill and along a rather dreary mile or two of the road. The sun had gone behind a cloud, and there were fields of coarse grass with only a few stunted trees. It was all so level that there was little to hold the eye, and the road was so straight that I could see a couple of miles ahead; and, to be quite frank, there was nothing very interesting anywhere. We may as well be honest with each other and agree that we sometimes come to drab patches in life. Then it is that we need more than ever something within us, for when there are few riches to be gathered along the road it is good to have some already in our minds and hearts. Happy are we if there is a gladness springing up inside us, a song singing in our thoughts when no lark sings in the sky, a portrait gallery of memories to look on when the way is across a countryside with few striking features, a close friendship for the lonely miles with One who is nearer than hands and feet.

I came to a dreary village with nothing to detain one five minutes, so I plodded on after asking my way to a village where I knew I was expected, and where I intended staying the night. I knew there would be a change of linen for me there, for I had arranged for it to be sent on, and I knew there would be an old-fashioned courtesy awaiting me.

I had lunch at a village inn where the landlord showed me a stick which his grandfather had used to good purpose when attacked by a footpad. 'He wouldn't have no nonsense, wouldn't my grandfather,' said the landlord. I went into the village street and patted a dog which came running up to me—we were friends in an instant. I crossed the square and saw a little maid of about five coming with a load of bread in a basket. She tripped along, smiling as she came. 'What a clever girl you are,' I said admiringly.

'Oh, I do nearly all the shopping,' she told me.

'How wonderful!'

'I have to,' she said gravely. 'I look after my daddy now we haven't got a mother.'

I went on, up the hill, and by a wood, mile after mile. Presently I heard the unusual music of hoofs beating on the hard highway. A man in a gig came jogging along.

'Care for a lift?' he called out.

'Thanks,' I said. 'I'll be glad of one.' (Notice how readily we fall from grace a second time. Conscience reminded me I was on a walking tour, but I argued that having travelled by 'bus there could be no harm—or rather, no more harm—in going a few miles in a gig.)

'Climb up, then,' said the man.

'I'm on my way to Thompson's,' I began.

'What, old Chris Thompson? Lives at the Grange? I know him, and proud to. I'm going right by his place, if the old mare can manage the two of us. She ought to, seeing one's an honest man.'

I glanced at the old farmer with his whiskery chin quivering with little dimples. 'You are very kind,' I said.

'Nay, don't begin thanking me at this end,' he said. 'For anything you know I may tip you out at the first corner we come to. You'll know that tale of the man who got a lift in a trap, and the horse bolted, and he offered the driver half-a-crown to be out, and the chap said, "Tha mun keep tha brass, lad, th'll be out for nowt in a minute." Well, he was. But that's an old tale. So you're going to see old Chris Thompson, eh? Grand old man he is. One of the best. I mind when he was farming a few hundred acres up Cramburn way, mostly oats and sheep. His shepherd comed to me when Thompson gave up farming. You'll know the tale about the farm hand that left suddenly?'

'No, I can't say I do.'

'Well, if you can't say, don't say it. He were a bit simple were the lad, and a friend met him one day and said, "Hello, got a holiday?" "No," said the lad. "I've left." "What, left?" "Aye, I'm not staying no longer. Not after what's happened." "Why, what's wrong?" his friend asked. "Wrong?" he says. "Well, a month or two ago an old cow died, and we'd nowt to eat but beef for weeks and weeks. Then a sheep died, and we'd nowt to eat but mutton. Now the old woman's died, so I'm leaving."'

I laughed.

'Oh, that's an old one,' he said. 'I reckon you'll know that story about the new minister who came to one of our village chapels, and announced the collection, and saw an old chap take it up, and then, just when he was putting the collection plate on a little table near the pulpit, the old chap pocketed half-a-crown from it. The young parson was upset, I can tell you, so he had a word with the good brother in the vestry, and the old chap just looked straight at him, and he says, "Nay, mister, don't worry yourself about that. I've led off with that there half-crown for thirty years." But maybe you've heard that before?'

'No,' I said, 'it's quite new. I don't know how you come to know so many tales.'

'Keep my ears open, you know,' he said, smiling. 'That reminds me of another story about a parson. A bit of an upstart, he was. He was on trial—it was a trial for those who listened, as well—and he marched up the pulpit steps as if he knew all there was to know about preaching, and gave out his text, and got no farther. He just broke down. He couldn't think of anything, and so he went down the pulpit steps with his head hanging and his face red, and a kindly old man comed up to him, and he said, "Eh lad, if only you'd gone up them steps same as you comed down, you'd have comed down same as you went up!"

'So you know old Thompson well, then?' he asked after laughing heartily at his own joke.

'Quite well. I knew him at Cramburn. I haven't been to see him since he retired.'

'No? Well, you'll find him just the same. I reckon it were a fine thing of him to go into another house at his time of life, and leave the old farm for John. He's doing very well is John, grand crop this year if all goes well. Got his head screwed on the right way. You'd know the youngest's married —she married Gilmour's eldest son. I reckon she's not gone as far as the old chap who was married four times, and then had a fifth, and the squire met him in the village one day and says, "Hey, John, I hear you're going to be married again?" "Aye," says John, "I am." "An' you've been married four times already?" the squire asks. "Aye," says John. The squire closed one eye, and looked at John, and he says shrewdly, "And you've always managed to get someone with a bit of money, eh?"

' "Well, yes," John told him. "Maybe I have, but what with bringing on 'em in, and carrying on 'em out, there ain't been much profit."

'And speaking about the squire reminds me of another who was riding in the village, and saw a lad with some ducks. "You've some fine ducks there, my lad," says he. "How often do you kill them?"

' "Nobbut once," said the lad. But maybe you've heard that before?'

I marvelled at his store of anecdotes.

'Yon's the Grange,' he said. 'It's been a pleasure to have you in the old gig. Not so fast as motor-cars, isn't the old mare, but she'll do. We all go sharper now than ever before, and get no farther. Sad, isn't it? That's what the patient felt like. "Doctor," he said, "I'm in a nervous condition. I feel like killing myself. What shall I do?"

' "Oh, nothing," said the doctor. "Leave it to me."

'Well, good afternoon, mister. Give William Badsworth's compliments to Christopher, and tell him I hope his shadow never grows less.'

A path between holly hedges brought me to the front door of a grave eighteenth-century house

with large windows and an air of dignity. The
door was wide open, and I could see the spacious
hall beyond, a big dog lying there, watching me
with brown eyes. I rang the bell, and a maid
came tripping along what sounded like miles of
flagstones. She knew me, and smiled in a friendly
way. She said would I go in, so I did; and a
moment later my old friend came to greet me, a
tall, slim, white-haired man dressed in a style of
last century. He was dignified, urbane, very
charming, a sort of Sir Roger de Coverley. That
he had been a farmer all his life no one would have
thought, yet the soil was bred in him, the patient
soil which never hurries, and is always faithful, the
soil which brings its best crops, not with sunshine
only, but with sunshine and storm together. I
will tell you presently how I came to know him;
but here I will only say that, as far as I can
remember, all the town-folk I have met—with the
exception of Christopher's wife—have lacked the
essential trait of this gentleman—his complete
satisfaction with life, and the humility his satisfaction bestowed on him.

'We are so glad you have come,' he was saying.
'Lottie insisted on your having the bedroom with
a window facing the orchard. She said she knew
you would like to hear the birds in the morning.
You see, she has not forgotten. Ah, here she is.'

'As young as ever,' said I.

He bowed, as if acknowledging the compliment
for her.

She took my hand, smiling radiantly. 'It will
be so pleasant to have you again,' she said.

'Christopher will be able to praise the country which he still thinks better than the town.' She laughed.

'But the town gave him the most precious thing in his house,' I replied gravely.

She glanced at Christopher. 'Did you hear?' she asked. 'Fancy his remembering that I came from London?'

I bent my head. 'Madam, could I forget?' I said reproachfully.

She wagged a finger at me. 'Now, no flattery . . . Christopher will not have it,' she said mischievously. Then she led me up the wide, richly-carpeted stairs. 'You must tell me how you like our new house,' she said. 'But that will come after dinner, when I will show you round. You see we have brought the old grandfather clock with us. We left John the big dresser you admired—the Elizabethan one. This is your room. You said you liked a four-poster bed, so here it is. And your parcel arrived yesterday—we opened it for you, and hung the clothes in the wardrobe. You'll see the orchard and the rose garden from the window, and we brought in the little table from the other room, we thought you might care to write here—knowing what shockingly late hours you keep.'

She was all vivaciousness and charm. Nearly seventy years had not taken her freshness from her, nor her graciousness. Vivacious indeed, and yet, it was a surface quality, for all the time her calm, peaceful spirit shone through. Her years had crowned her with peace. You never saw a face with more repose in it than hers when she was listening to you, never one more intensely alive when she was telling you something—the lips wrinkling into a quick smile, her eyes flashing a glance that would have caught any man fifty years before.

I thanked her.

She left me to remove the stain of travel. This was not merely a phrase; it was an actual fact. I had a hot bath. I put myself into clean clothes. I felt a new man, and found myself wearing a collar and tie instead of the open shirt I had worn all the week. I also caught myself whistling a hymn to the old tune 'Sagiora.' I stopped to look at myself in the mirror, and to ask why that tune should have come unbidden into my thoughts.

I smiled to see the little oak table with carved legs, and the Chippendale chair by it. The dear folk here evidently thought I wrote every day of my life. There were two candles on the table, each in an old iron candlestick.

I went downstairs and found Christopher walking slowly up and down the lawn beyond the French windows of the drawing-room. There was a sundial, the fragrance of flowers, quietness. 'Dinner will be served in a few minutes,' said my host.

'I am ready for it when it comes,' I told him. 'I have missed a meal to-day. By the way, I came the last mile or two with a most entertaining friend of yours, a Mr. Badsworth.'

'William? Ah, yes, an excellent man.'

'And full of stories. He gave me a lift in his gig, and I was glad of it. It is years since I rode behind a horse.'

'Yes, I dare say. William does not take to motor-cars. He is like me in that respect. Lottie and I prefer a trap to a car, as you know. Edward insists on taking us in his car when he comes over, and John motors us over to Cramburn now and then. But we like the pony and trap best. Old Dobbin is with us still, though we have put him out to grass now. He grows older every day—as his master.'

We went indoors. The dining-room, panelled in oak, and lighted by four big windows, had a polished floor with brightly-coloured rugs. The table, beautiful with glass and silver, was set off with a black bowl of sweet peas. Christopher stepped forward to draw back a chair for his wife, doing it naturally and unthinkingly, and with that quiet and unstudied courtesy which a Scarlet Pimpernel might have shown a queen. She did not omit to thank him. They sat facing each other; I had my back to two of the windows. My host bowed his head. 'For all Thy mercies to us this day, and all our days, Lord, make us truly thankful,' he said.

'Amen,' said his wife.

She talked quickly while Christopher carved the fowl and ham, and I thought perhaps she wished to divert my attention from my host who carved best when least observed. She asked about my tour, and where I had been, and if I had been comfortable at the places where I had stayed the night. She laughed at the tales William Badsworth had told, saying, there was a chatterbox for you, and that as long as William lived no one could say women did all the talking. Every now and then she appealed to Christopher for confirmation, as if, indeed, she were anxious that he should not feel neglected, or think she were giving too many of her own opinions without consulting him. Christopher was slow and grave, she quick and light-hearted, yet both had that deeper quality of calm wherein their spirits met.

'It was a terrible uprooting,' she was explaining. 'I mean leaving Cramburn. But we thought it best. They have children, you know, and it was better for John to be near a good school. That is partly why we came here. It is a beautiful house, and I am sure you will like it.'

'I like it already,' I said.

'But of course it can never be quite the same,' she said. 'We had been in the other over thirty years. We loved Cramburn, didn't we, Christopher?'

'Yes, it kept a bit of weather out; but this is a fine old house.'

'Yes, old,' said Lottie. 'That is true. Old and substantial, as Christopher said. There was no bathroom in it till we had one put in. I had the old stone sinks taken out and porcelain ones put in; and we had hot water laid on, of course.'

'You move with the times,' I told her.

She laughed gaily. 'Ah no,' she said, 'you are mistaken. We move behind the times. You see, we have neither gas nor electricity, only lamps and candles. They have electricity in the village, and we could have had it if we had wanted it, but Christopher—he's so old-fashioned, you know (I'm only joking, darling) —preferred lamps and candles. He says he can see better by candle-light than by electric-light. did you ever hear such nonsense?'

'No, Lottie,' he declared, 'that is not what I said, my dear. I said I liked to see *you* better by candle-light than by electric-light . . .'

'There now!' she declared triumphantly, 'was there ever such a cruel man? He knows that he will see all my wrinkles by electric-light!' Christopher put down his knife and fork and looked at her over the sweet peas. She laughed back at him. 'I know what you are going to say,' she said. 'You are going to say it was by candle-light you saw me first. Isn't that so?'

He nodded.

'I knew. He is a dear, but frightfully old-fashioned, and so very sentimental.'

He beamed on her. 'It's a weakness you haven't managed to shake me out of, dear,' he retorted. Then, turning to me he said, 'I told you the story of our first meeting up at Cramburn Hall, didn't I?'

'Yes,' I said, 'I remember it, and how you saw your wife as she came down the stairs, and fell in love with her at first sight. It was very wonderful.'

'I was only seventeen,' she said very softly, sighing a little. 'And Christopher was only a year older.'

'And we had to wait seven years before we

could be married,' Christopher added. 'I told you that?'

'No,' I said, 'I didn't know that. You remember the family came in that evening when you were telling me about it. I have always thought the bit you told me romantic enough to go in a book, and I knew you were a long time before you were married, though I didn't know it was quite so long.'

'Seven years,' he said. 'Nearly four hundred Sundays.'

'Why Sundays?'

'We wrote to each other every Sunday. We only missed twice—once when Lottie's sister was ill, and the Sunday my mother died. Seven years of waiting and hoping, and looking forward. Lottie would not leave her father—he was ill nearly all the time; she had promised never to leave him. It was her way.' I saw him smile at her again.

'They were not wasted years, were they?'

'Nothing need be wasted in God's world,' he said. 'Nothing. Sometimes they seemed bitter years. In the first four we saw each other only three days, all told. But the years were not wasted. They made our love grow stronger and fiercer, and perhaps finer. They taught us to grow in mind and spirit, each more like the other. We came to love the same things, to want the same things, to think in the same way, didn't we, Lottie?'

'Yes, Christopher.'

'It tried our patience a bit?'

'But deepened our love.'

'We've never had a wrong word, have we, Lottie?'

'How could we?' she whispered.

'Marriage has brought us all that's best in life, my dear?'

'Everything, Christopher. Our happiness has been all the greater for being shared. We have had six children—and one that went early, to be ready to give us a welcome in heaven.'

'We've given and taken, Lottie.' (He seemed to have forgotten I was there.) 'You've borne with my weaknesses, my dear.'

She left her chair, came round the table, leaned over him, patted his cheeks, and kissed the top of his head. 'You stupid old thing,' she said—and there were tears in her eyes. 'Haven't I led you a dance all the time? Why, look, I've turned your hair quite white!'

He had closed his hands over hers, and was looking up into her face. 'Lottie,' he said, 'I wonder if we've been too happy, you and me?'

She looked at him. I saw their eyes meet. They might have been seventeen and eighteen, these two. And I felt as if heaven had opened, and I had seen love enthroned.

She returned to her chair, and asked me what I would take, and glanced at me laughingly. 'Did you ever see two such queer old folk?' she asked.

'Never,' said I.

We finished dinner with hardly another word.

'You know,' said my host as he pushed his

plate from him and folded his serviette, 'I believe in long courtships, and I think the best thing that can happen before marriage is misfortune. It makes marriage more sacred, more precious. Have we all finished?

'Lord, for the blessings of this table, and for all Thy gracious mercies to us this day, and every day, we are humbly thankful.'

'Amen,' said his wife.

Then we rose. My host holding out his arm, led my hostess to the lounge with a gallantry that charmed me.

After coffee had been served my hostess showed me round the house. 'We took it partly because George has a big family,' she explained, 'five children, all girls, you know, and we thought when our day was done it would be nice for them to come and live here. We have made this into the lounge. There are two huge kitchens, and a wonderful wash-house, and an apple room. The stick-house is big enough for a stable. What do you think of my larder? Isn't it wonderful? And the dairy—just look at it. We don't use it as a dairy, of course, but it will come in handy for George some day. Christopher lets me keep chickens, though he said he wouldn't at first. We're having a tennis-court made. It will be so handy for the children when they come over. I love the orchard. We had a wonderful crop of apples last year—our first ingathering, so we gave them all away except about twenty stones. The minister made a pyramid of them in the chapel at the harvest festival. He said it was the most wonderful heap they had ever seen. He is a very delightful man, but I am afraid he is not as energetic as the vicar you were telling me about, the one who had lost his wife, I mean. Poor man, I wish he would marry the lady with the white hair, it would be so beautiful for them . . .'

So she chattered on, taking me over the house, and into the garden where we were joined by Christopher, who came out with a shawl, fearing that the air might be rather chilly for her.

The evening passed quickly, graciously, calmly, uneventfully; and when the grandfather clock on the stairs struck ten, I begged to be excused, for I knew they always retired early, and would read a chapter from the Bible, and say their prayers together before going up to bed.

'I wish you a very good night,' said my host gravely.

'And beautiful thoughts to go to sleep on,' said my hostess, smiling.

I did not need a candle to show me the way upstairs, but when I had half undressed, and had stood awhile by the open window, and looked beyond the garden and the orchard to the valley I had crossed, I struck a match, and lighted both my candles. Two shadows sprang into the room to keep me company, but I had no fear of them. I took out pen and paper, for I had a mind to write by candle-light. As a child, a candle had kept the darkness out of my eyes when my mother had kissed me and left me alone in the quiet room. Perhaps that is why I love candle-light still. I believe in progress with all my heart, but I think

gas and electricity and lamps and torches, all but
the flickering firelight, are without that gentle,
friendly, golden charm of candles. They give a
soft, caressing light; and it is strange to think that
it was perhaps by such a light that Caiaphas
questioned Christ—the loveliest light men have
ever made shedding its radiance over the beginning
of the darkest crime of all the years. By this light,
then, I wrote, making a few notes about the
adventures of the day, and afterwards recording
how I had first come to know these charming
people whose guest I was.

I walked into their lives by chance one day
in June four years before I saw the Grange. I
was staying in the country with a friend, and one
evening I happened to walk out alone. I chose a
green lane, and coming to a turn in it (for it is a
long lane that has no turning) I saw two lovers
arm-in-arm. Had I been a truly gallant gentleman, I should straightway have turned about and
walked in the opposite direction, leaving them to
enjoy the lane alone. But I did not turn about;
and, if the whole story must be told, I did not even
slacken my pace, but went on, slowly overtaking
them.

They walked in the pleasant evening sunshine,
and sometimes, as I saw plainly, he bent his head
very near to hers; and, as I drew closer (treacherous
conspirator that I was) I caught the sound of happy
laughter, low and musical. They did not hurry,
these two. Her arm was in his, and I think she
leaned on it a little. Once, at a high point in the
lane, they stopped to admire the view. So base was

I that I stopped also, and when they moved on, I followed. There was a seat a little way ahead, and I guessed they were making for it. I was not wrong. They walked over the grass, and sat down on the seat whereon more than one generation of lovers had carved their initials. Very close they sat, two lovers in a green lane, the sunshine all about them. Both were white-haired.

When I had come up to them I smiled, and said that it was a lovely evening. Then I made as if to go on, but when they smiled back, I stood still and confessed that I had been walking behind them, and that I had been watching them, and that what I had seen had made me very happy. Then they looked at each other, and the woman said, 'We forgive you for spying on us. We love this lane. It means a great deal to us. We have taken a walk along it at least once every summer for thirty years, haven't we, Christopher?'

'Yes, Lottie,' the man answered, 'we have.'

'And you have been happy all the time, I can see,' I said.

'Yes,' said the man, 'I believe we have, though it's only fair to say that Lottie, here, is the worst wife I've ever had.'

'And my young man,' said the smiling lady, 'is a terrible responsibility.' (I saw her hand gently patting his as she spoke, as if to assure him she was only making fun of him.)

Thus I met Christopher and Lottie; and when I returned to my friend's house I told him of my adventure, and he laughed, and said he was not surprised, adding that he would take me over to see them the next day. So we went to Cramburn Farm, and there we were received with courtesy, and made very welcome. As I happened to know something of that part of London from which Lottie had come years before, she and I quickly struck up a friendship; and as one of the girls was interested in books, as I have always been, and was writing a thesis on a subject with which I happened to be familiar, I gave her what help I could, and in consequence was asked over for Christmas. Thus a friendship ripened.

This evening — as I carefully noted — I had heard one of the secrets of their happiness. I had listened to Christopher speaking in that deliberate way of his, and had seen the smiles exchanged between these two. I had felt that marriage was a wonderful, a beautiful thing. And I thought, if ever I write a book about my tour I will give this incident pride of place. At the risk of tiring the reader, I will set on record my host's story of his waiting, for perhaps these pages may fall into the hands of some who, having grown sophisticated, have come to think matrimony a cheap thing, a playing at fast and loose, an experiment in which each tries to get something for himself or herself, and is unwilling to share fortune and misfortune. Old-fashioned these two are, to be sure, but I think they help us to see what marriage can be.

All this I thought and wrote by candle-light. I thought of my host with his fine face, a face different from many that are seen to-day, a face with no lines of care, no anxiety, no anger, no knitting of the brows, no hardening of the mouth, nothing sensual, nothing mean. He was a simple man, a man who was nothing more than a farmer with only a fair education, yet he was a gentleman.

And she, all graciousness, winsome, attractive still, lively, and yet singularly placid. These two might have come from some sixteenth-century portrait gallery, dignified, punctilious in courtesy, selfless, beautiful in face and spirit. I put down my pen and bowed my head, and asked God's blessing on the quiet house, and on the two who for so long had loved each other and given love to others, enriching the world with children who had their parents' spirit.

The clock on the stairs struck midnight—slowly. Why should it hurry? I put away my papers, stuffing them into my haversack. Midnight! So it was Sunday morning! I sought for, and found, Thomas à Kempis, and opening him at random I read:

'O Lord, in the simplicity of my heart, I offer myself unto Thee this day, in humble submission, for a sacrifice of perpetual praise, and to be Thy servant for ever. I offer unto Thee, O Lord, all my sins, offences which I have committed before Thee, from the day wherein I first could sin to this hour. Cleanse my conscience from all offences, and restore to me again Thy grace, which I have lost by sin, forgiving me all my offences, and receiving me mercifully to the kiss of peace. I offer up also unto Thee all whatsover is good in me, although it be very small and imperfect, that Thou mayest amend and sanctify it. Make it grateful and acceptable unto Thee, and always perfect it more and more; and bring me also, who am a slothful and unprofitable creature, to a good and blessed end. Have mercy, O Lord, have mercy on those that crave Thy mercy, give grace unto them that stand in need thereof, and make us such as that we may be counted worthy to enjoy Thy grace and go forward to life eternal. Amen.'

Then I prayed:

'Most merciful Father, give me an understanding heart that I may read Thee in all things and in all men. Give me a grace that all men may read Thee in me. Keep me through this night, and in the morning may I gladly rise to do Thy will, or bear it, and to show forth Thy praise not only with my lips, but in my life; and this I ask through Him who loves me still. Amen.'

And when I had undressed, I blew out the candles, drew back the curtains, and fell asleep in the starlight.

CHAPTER VII

Sunday in the country; I attend service in a little chapel; hear a sermon from a grocer; doze in the sunshine; meet four sons and two daughters and their wives and husbands and children; have tea with a merry company; am one of a rare congregation which made a sanctuary of a lounge.

THE QUIETNESS of Sunday morning woke me.

That may seem odd, but I think it was literally true. I remember, as a boy, staying with an uncle in a village among the Yorkshire hills; and even in those days I used to think I could hear the silence of Sunday. My uncle's house was on a hillside, and in the valley immediately below were a dozen woollen mills, the noise from them distinctly heard night and day in my uncle's house. But Sunday morning had no roar of machinery, no six o'clock siren. All was still, though sometimes one would hear a cock crowing near at hand, and then, almost like an echo, another crowing far off.

So, when I woke at the Grange, I was conscious of the stillness. Sunday has gone from our towns and cities, but it lingers in the country. Its benediction is there still. I heard a few birds whistling and chattering in the orchard below my window. I heard the church clock strike seven, and then eight. A full hour I lay there, letting the silence of the world and of the sleeping house sink into my spirit. 'Be still, and know that I am God.'

Sunday morning meant breakfast at nine instead of eight. At quarter past eight there came a gentle tap at my door. 'It is quarter past eight, sir, and a fine morning,' said a voice outside.

Even that was old-fashioned.

I was down to breakfast at a minute to nine. My host trusted I had slept well. My hostess trusted I had not burnt the candles away.

We breakfasted leisurely, and afterwards, instead of a grace, Christopher offered a prayer. 'Heavenly Father,' said he, 'we thank Thee for Thy blessings to us, more numerous and richer than we deserve. Teach us, Lord, to remember others as Thou hast remembered us. Keep us humble with our happiness, sympathethic, and understanding. Bless our dear children, and their children, and all that is theirs. Bless our guest, and grant him a harvest of good things at the end of his journey. To those who minister to us in this house, and beyond it, give a sense of Thy nearness. Help us, Lord, to live more worthily, and strengthen us for the way that lies before. So, Father, may we all do Thy will below, and meet with joy in heaven. We ask it through the name of Thy dear Son. Amen.'

Then, after repeating the Lord's prayer, we left the table, Christopher to walk in his garden, Lottie to see that lunch would be prepared, and I to my room to read a word or two of Thomas à Kempis.

A little after ten we took the field path to the village, to attend a service in the Methodist chapel. A very small building it was, and simple as a Quaker meeting house. Not more than a score of people were present, but the service was memorable. We had a 'local preacher', a grocer who lived eight miles away, a simple, honest soul with a fine face and a grave manner. He had a way of clasping his hands and looking up as if he believed that God would put the words into his mouth. We began with an old Methodist hymn, 'O for a thousand tongues to sing,' and it was sung with warmth and sincerity. There were three in the choir, one a venerable man who kept time with his right hand which was continually smiting the book-rest in front of him. He sang with emphasis on every other beat. My host took the tenor parts. There were two boys in corduroy behind us, and three women who looked as if they had lived in the country all their lives, their faces were so round and red.

We had a prayer, a long one, in which the grocer wrestled with the Lord, and implored forgiveness for his manifold sins.

'Amen,' said the old man in the choir.

'Lord,' said the preacher, 'we haven't been all we might have been, not any of us. Lord, take me for example. Thou knowest I was impatient with the errand lad, and little wonder, Lord, for he's enough to drive anybody out of their senses; but, O Lord, I ought to have more patience. Lord, I am nothing without Thee. Less than nothing. Do Thou help me and guide me. And all others as well, Lord, for most of them are little better than me, and we all need Thy help, and, praise be to Thee, Thou wilt give us the help we need!'

'Hallelujah!'—from the old man in the choir.

There followed another hymn, and a Bible reading about Peter sleeping on the housetop and Cornelius sending for him. Then the preacher said, 'Friends, we'll sing a hymn that gave me a new life when I was not much older than these dear lads who are with us this morning; and oh, I'm glad indeed the Lord has moved in their hearts and brought them to the house of prayer. We can't come too soon. Lord bless them, Lord bless them. Now, we'll sing:

> Thou Great Redeemer, dying Lamb,
>   We love to hear of Thee.

Isn't it true, friends?

> No music's like Thy charming name,
>   Nor half so sweet can be.

Let us rise and sing!'

We rose and sang, and when we had finished the last verse, the old man in the choir was carried away with emotion, and started the verse again:

> 'When we appear in yonder cloud,
>   With all that favoured throng,
> Then will we sing more sweet, more loud,
>   And Christ shall be our song!
>   And Christ shall be our song!'

After another prayer the collection was taken up by the caretaker who was also a trustee and superintendent of the Sunday school. We sang again, and then the preacher announced his text. 'You'll find my text, friends,' he said, 'in the

Gospel of St. Mark, the sixteenth chapter, and the fifteenth verse. "Go ye into all the world, and preach the gospel."

'That is what the Lord said long ago to those about Him, and He says it to us to-day. He said it to me, praise to His name; and I've tried to do it, and I'm still trying. "Go ye . . ." Can you go to preach if you have nothing to tell? Well then, before you go you must have something to give others, and before you give you must receive. The first thing to do is to get on your knees and ask Jesus to show Himself to you in all His beauty; and when you see Him you'll fall in love with Him. You'll talk with Him as I talk with Him of an evening when the shop's shut up and I get a bit of peace, and there aren't any more pounds of sugar to weigh. I talk with him, and He talks with me. It is a blessed communion.'

'Amen, and Amen,' said the old man in the choir.

'Aye, my friend, you'd need say Amen. Isn't it blessed? Haven't we found it so, you and me? Can a man escape his sins? Oh wondrous grace that can't be bought, but is given to all that come and ask in sincerity and in truth! We have to have an experience—conversion—before we can convert the world. Friends, the day I saw my wife for the first time I was a changed man. I lived for her. That's what happens when we see Jesus in His beauty, only it is more wonderful still.

'So, my firstly, is being converted ourselves.

'Getting Christ into our own lives is the first thing, but He is so big that we can't keep Him in our little lives any more than you can put a gallon into a quart jug; it's bound to run over. So, when we've got Jesus in our hearts He overflows, and we become preachers.

'Ah, but I hear some of you say, "That's all very well, mister, but I can't stand up in a pulpit and preach. I can't even pray in a prayer meeting!" Would to God we had more prayer meetings. England will never be pure till we have meetings for prayer, for out-pouring and in-pouring of the Spirit.'

'Amen!'

'*We* know that, don't we, my old friend? Isn't it at a prayer meeting that we bring all our sins to the Lord, and the sins of others, and get forgiveness for our own short-comings, and grace to bear with others—and what a power of grace we need! "But," you'll say, "how can we go and preach to all the world? Can we leave our homes and farms and hay-making, and go and preach to Hindus, and black folk, and all the rest of God's great family?" Ah, my friends, the Lord has His own ministers. Some of us preach in pulpits, and a sorry job we make of it; but we preach in our houses, and in our shops, and in our dairies, and while we're hay-making. Aye, we can do that. We don't need books or texts. All we need is Christ in our hearts, and His love shining in our faces— for it *does* shine there, and even Moses wist not that he had been with God. What we are, and what we do, and what we say, and how we live, all this is preaching, and by this we win souls for the Lord, and preach by our lives.

'The Lord help us all to do it. Amen, and Amen.'

Then we sang,

> 'All praise to our redeeming Lord,
>   Who joins us by His grace,
> And bids us, each to each restored,
>   Together seek His face.
>
> He bids us build each other up;
>   And, gathered into one,
> To our high calling's glorious hope
>   We hand in hand go on.
>
> We all partake the joy of one,
>   The common peace we feel,
> A peace to sensual minds unknown,
>   A joy unspeakable.'

I watched and listened. The sunshine came in through the plain windows, and beyond the open door I could see sheep on the hills. I looked at the old man in the choir—his face radiant. I heard Lottie singing. I saw Christopher keeping his eyes on her as he sang without his hymn book, for he knew every word. I looked up at the face of the preacher. I felt a baptism of the Spirit resting on me like cloven tongues of fire. I thought there had never been a simpler or a more sincere service. I wondered what the sceptics would have thought, and if the psychologists would consider that we were all suffering from falsely induced emotions. I wondered. . . but we were singing the last verse . . .

> 'And if our fellowship below
>   In Jesus be so sweet,
> What heights of rapture shall we know
>   When round His throne we meet!'

'The Lord bless each one, and go with us to our homes; the Lord comfort us and strengthen us according to our need; the Lord be with us evermore; and the grace of Our Lord Jesus Christ, and the love of God, and the fellowship of the Holy Spirit, abide with us all. Amen.'

The gathering broke up decently. The preacher stood at the door to shake hands with us as we went out. The caretaker locked the church, and glanced at me. 'We've had a *helpful* sermon,' he remarked.

'Yes,' I said, 'very.'

Then he went off, for he was entertaining the preacher. I stood apart from the two or three people who were talking with my host and hostess. Yes, the caretaker had been right. He had used the right word, our gathering together *had* been helpful.

It was a quiet walk across the fields to the Grange. After lunch I took a book into the garden, and read and dozed in a deck-chair; and before I knew where I was I heard voices and found that the first contingent of the weekly invading army had arrived. You must know that the removal from Cramburn to the Grange had made no difference to the established custom of Sunday afternoon. Every Sunday the four sons and two daughters with their respective wives and husbands, and their children, came over to the Grange. There were seventeen grandchildren, and they always had the first sitting down at tea, the older folk looking after them. Then, when they had feasted, they went into the garden if the weather were fine, one of the sons and his wife playing with them while the rest of the family sat down in the big dining-room, the long table presided over by Christopher, Lottie and John's wife pouring out the tea. It was a custom never departed from, except at a holiday time, and it was a re-union of wonderful power and charm.

There was John the eldest son, a man with the bearing of his father and the vivacity of his mother. His wife, a pretty woman, had a special place in everyone's affections, for she had a genius for making people happy. There was Joseph, who motored over every Sunday and brought his wife— a very delightful little lady, so delicate that she looked almost too rare a spirit to live long, so eager you thought her soul would jump out of her small body. George was the giant of the family, a big, broad fellow who farmed seven hundred acres, and could plough a straight furrow, and was not above mending his own fences, and cleaning out his own stables, and had an old-fashioned view about farming, which was that you could still make the land pay if you and your wife (for that slip of a girl of his worked as hard as any labourer's wife) did your bit, and didn't expect the farm to keep you like a lord. There was Michael, paler than the rest. He was a solicitor in the nearest big town, and had a growing clientele. His wife was an M.A., and could talk with authority on almost any topic. It was these two whose turn it was to look after the children while the others were at tea, and as four of the youngsters were their own I guessed they would know very well how to keep the company in order. Joan was the elder of the two married

daughters. Her husband, a farmer living a few
miles away, was a handsome young fellow with a
face which looked as if it never needed shaving.
He seemed very self-conscious, and would flush up
half a dozen times in an hour. The others tor-
mented him without mercy, but he took it all in
good part, and declared that Joan led him a dog's
life, and was making him grow thin and haggard.
Margaret, the youngest of all, had been married
one year only. It was she whom I had helped with
her thesis that first summer, but there had been
no need to bother as to whether she took her
degree or not, for she had married an estate agent,
and had been domesticated in five minutes. Her
husband managed the affairs of one of the biggest
landowners in the neighbourhood; and his thin
face, bright eyes behind horn-rimmed spectacles,
and precise manner suggested that he was a most
efficient business man.

We were a big party. But there was room to
spare, and everyone was friendly. The conversation was interesting, and there was humour
enough, all of it kindly. It seemed that, apart from
little taunts and thrusts which fell harmlessly,
everyone admired and respected everyone else.
They had all been received with quiet earnestness—
a warm handgrip from Christopher, a kiss from
Lottie. There were queries about the children, and
every grandchild, some of them in their teens,
had to come to grandad and grannie, and talk
with them. They did it willingly.

After tea everyone helped to clear away and
wash up, for the maids had a holiday Sunday

afternoon and evening. Then chairs were carried into the spacious lounge, and we had a little service—one of the most beautiful I have ever known. Two of the sons were local preachers, and after a hymn, and a prayer from Christopher, we had a reading by one of the grandchildren, Rose, who read from the family Bible in a clear, sweet voice. Then we had another hymn, and it was stirring indeed to hear those young, strong voices, the deep bass of Joan's husband, the tenor of Christopher and three of the sons, and the soprano and contralto of the daughters-in-law, all harmonizing perfectly. We had a children's hymn, 'I think when I read that sweet story of old,' and the little ones sang the first half of each verse, and the rest of us came in for the second half; and another hymn went to the tune 'Wareham,' and the sopranos soared up as if on angels' wings, and the tenors improvized, and I think any one passing along the road at that hour must have thought that heaven had come to earth.

It was Michael who gave us a ten minutes' sermon about the love of God, a simple talk which came from his heart; and when he had finished we knelt in silent prayer, and then joined in singing, 'The day thou gavest, Lord, is ended.' As the last notes died away we all stood silent in the evening sunshine, heads bowed while old Christopher, his voice trembling slightly, pronounced the benediction. Who knew how many more benedictions he would pronounce?

It was all over by seven o'clock, and as two

of the families had young children, they motored off soon afterwards, but some stayed later, and John and his wife did not go till after nine.

I talked with many of them. I heard about crops, about the felling of trees the winter before, about Michael's concern for his mother who had looked rather too flushed, and about Joan's fears lest these big gatherings were too much for the old folk. She had more than once suggested that they should go alternate Sundays, half one Sunday, and half the next. I was interested in the solicitor's story of a transfer of land for which the rent had long been a red rose every first of January. He told me the deed was valid only so long as a straw of wheat was pinned to the signature. I heard from Margaret's husband about the difficulties of landowners, and how Lord X had had to sell much of his timber.

At last the re-union was over, and tranquillity returned to the Grange. I knew my host and hostess were tired, and after a few minutes' conversation I went up to bed. I did not take out Thomas, neither *Virginibus*. But I sat in my room, and thought of all the happenings of the day. I felt that I had been recharged with energy, mental and spiritual. I felt that Sunday had made me a wiser, a richer, a humbler man. I felt that whatever freedom Sunday might bring for many people, whatever excitement it might give them, however it might be spent, it could never supply more inspiration than this unforgettable day. Prayer and praise, thanksgiving and consecration, graciousness, understanding, new ideas, unity, blessing, music, knowledge, rest, all these had come into this one day. Old-fashioned it may have been. To many it could never appeal. But I wondered if in all England, if in cathedral and mission, in palace and hall, in the open air or the amusement centre, anyone anywhere could have drunk more deeply of the rich, red wine of life than I?

I left my candles unlighted. I was asleep before darkness fell.

CHAPTER VIII

I climb a hill and think about the high places of the earth; talk with a gentleman of the road; am informed that one should never miss 'a hopportunity'; help a charming motorist in distress; travel by car (almost) against my will; talk with a doomed man; and set out on a wild-goose chase.

In spite of their persuasions, I left the Grange before nine the next morning. They would have had me stay a few days, but I pointed out that I was a pilgrim with no abiding city at the moment; and that being refreshed in body, mind, and spirit, it behoved me to plod on. So, with sandwiches in my haversack, and a benediction bestowed with smiles, and with their God-speed (as if I had been blazing a trail through virgin jungles) I left them, though Christopher insisted on coming with me to the farther end of the village, where we shook hands.

All the dreary country was five miles behind, and among the hills was richness, and an ever-changing scene. Sometimes I left the wheat-fields and came up to hayfields where the hay-makers had been at work, though the morning dew had been too heavy for them to begin at that early hour. I came to a village in a hollow and saw a smith putting an iron rim on a cart-wheel. I came to a village on a hill-side where all but one of the houses looked into a valley with a stream running by the grey walls of a ruined abbey, the remnant of a glory England had known six hundred years ago, and a place where monks had praised God and hidden from men. I thought of Tennyson, and of how the old order changeth and giveth place to new, lest one good custom should corrupt the world. I walked on, easily and steadily, without counting the miles; and presently I approached a very steep hill which made me sigh to look at it. I promised myself a rest at the top, and I thought of the sandwiches in my haversack. So up I went, looking at my feet that I might not see how much more of the hill there was to climb. The flies danced round my face and neck, and the dust made me thirsty, and the calves of my legs ached with the steepness of the climb, but I went up and up, and managed somehow to smile to a fellow who was coming down; and at the last I reached the top where I looked over the wide countryside, and over the trees whose highest branches did not reach my feet. I saw the white road quivering in the hot air, and the river shining among the woods, and I thought that a hill-top was indeed a very blessed spot.

I sat down on a green bank and unpacked my sandwiches. My thoughts gathered round hills, and I began to realize how much there was to meditate upon. My mind went back to childhood's days, and I thought of the fairy-tale of the Princess of the Glass Hill. I remembered those two odd little people, Jack and Jill, of whom we read that they went up a hill to fetch a pail of water. Thinking of them I must needs remember

> The grand old Duke of York,
>   He had ten thousand men,
> He marched them up to the top of the hill,
>   And marched them down again.

And why shouldn't he? The troops ended *where* they began, no doubt, but they did not end *as* they began, or, rather, they should not have done, for surely they would be better soldiers for the training? There was a man once who was washed off a ship by a big wave, and washed on again by another. He ended where he began, but not as he began; and one would think he would have a bit more depth in his life after the experience than before it. One would think so.

Be that as it may, can any of us think of hills without recalling the poem

> Up the airy mountain,
>   Down the rushy glen,
> We daren't go a-hunting
>   For fear of little men,
> Wee folk, good folk,
>   Trooping altogether,
> Green jacket, red cap,
>   And white owl's feather.

Fairies? What a world of wonder we lived in when we believed in fairies, and looked for them. I thought of G. K. Chesterton's *Napoleon of Notting Hill*, and of a hill outside Nottingham where, says tradition, the wise men of Gotham solemnly rolled cheeses down to market. With Stevenson in my pocket, I must needs be transported over the hills and far away to *Treasure Island*, and to Spy-Glass Hill therein.

There was *Puck of Pook's Hill*, you remember, and there was the *Lass of Richmond Hill*. Who had not stood on Box Hill near London, and thought of the Canterbury Pilgrims who crossed the river close by, of Nelson's last farewell at Burford Bridge, of Robert Louis Stevenson who loved it all, of Sheridan and Keats whose spirits haunt it, and of George Meredith, than whom no man ever loved it more?

It was round Hill 60 that some of the most terrible fighting in the mad days of the War took place. There was fighting done, too, on the Heights of Abraham where Wolfe died after a great victory; at Edgehill where Harvey thought about blood while the king helped to spill it. To Englishmen there can be few spots more tragic than Tower Hill where some of the worst and the best men have died.

Bunyan has given us an immortal picture of the Hill of Difficulty, and Tennyson stirs us with his vision of eternal change:

> The hills are shadows and they flow
>   From form to form, and nothing stands;
>   They melt like mist, the solid lands,
> Like clouds they shape themselves and go.

We might lose ourselves among the hills of the Bible, the dwelling-places of God. Moses met

God on a mountain. The Psalmist says, 'I will lift up mine eyes unto the hills,' and we read that the strength of the hills is His also. There was Carmel where Elijah won a great victory, and Mount Zion where the people were to come with singing, and Mars' Hill where Paul preached, and the little hill to which all the world has turned for centuries, a hill where One who, being lifted up, has drawn all men unto Himself.

> There is a green hill far away,
>   Without a city wall,
> Where the dear Lord was crucified,
>   Who died to save us all.

But for hills the earth would be a plain with no joy of climbing heights, no spacious vision. I am glad there are hills.

' 'Scuse me, mister, but you haven't a pipeful of baccy, 'ave yer?'

I turned sharply to see a gentleman of the road in a bowler hat and a tweed suit a size too big for him. He wore a long, threadbare overcoat, and I gathered that all his worldly wealth and possessions were in the capacious pockets. 'Just a pipeful as one gentleman to another, mister.'

I handed him my pouch. 'Help yourself,' I said.

'By all means, mister, by all means. That's 'ansome, mister, that is.' He sat down rather nearer to me than I cared, but I did not move. 'Hexaminin' the view, hey? Wunderful, ain't it? Me poor old feet prevents me enjoying

Nature to the full. They hakes something hawful. How's yours?'

I took the pouch and began filling my pipe. 'Tired,' I said, 'but bearable.'

He looked at me sideways. 'I suppose you hain't gotta match?'

'As one gentleman to another,' I said, 'I think I can provide you with a match.'

'Thank you kindly, mister. Life hain't so bad when there's a few decent folk knocking about. A bit before you hove in sight, mister, I was just saying to myself, "Bill, you could 'ave had a smoke to 'elp your poor old feet if you'd 'ad some tobacco, and somebody 'ad 'appened to give you a match," I were sayin' them very words, mister, and there you was.'

'Remarkable,' I murmured. 'I'll borrow a match if you don't mind.'

Reluctantly he returned the box, and lay back against the green bank, blowing clouds of smoke into the air.

'It hain't every day I smokes this 'ere kind of tobacco,' he observed after a long pause. 'It's a honour to this 'ere bowl. It's mostly twist as I smokes, and I does it hout of gratitude to the Goviment.'

'Oh?'

'I don't forget the Goviment,' he said. 'It's done a lot for me, it 'as.' He puffed away fiercely for a few minutes. Then he added, 'Done its best to remember me, it 'as. Wanted to give me a pension for noble services in the War, it did. Tried 'ard, it did, but it hain't remembered yet. So busy payin'

theirselves at White'all, sir, they hain't no time
for other fellers. I'm grateful for them trying to
remember, mister. That's why I smokes a good
deal—when I 'appen to have the twist, and the
matches. I don't like to think o' them dear fellers
at White'all havin' to spend their precious time
catching bluebottles in the hoffices, so I smokes
twist, sir, and it kills a few of 'em hoff—the bluebottles, not the fellers, mind you; and so there's
less flies' heggs about, and less flies in consequence,
and so maybe there's a few less bluebottles
a-buzzing in them hoffices, so mayhap they'll
come across my name about the hend of the
century, and make the money hover to me great
great grandchildren, if they 'urries hup.' He
smoked in silence.

'You are very thoughtful,' I remarked.

He nodded. 'That's the first mark hov a
gentleman,' he said. 'Thoughtfulness! A gentleman's halways thinking of hothers, and not of
'isself.' Then, with a sly glance at me. 'You seem
to 'ave taken to the road a bit yourself, mister.'

'Yes,' I said. 'I've been tramping along a bit
lately.'

'You're not one of these 'ere blessed 'ikers?
No, I can see you hain't. You'd a moved hon be
now if you 'ad been. Most hov 'em's been brought
up in cotton wool, poor darlin's. It makes me
'eart break for 'em. You hask 'em for a match,
and they can't find one in their bundles. Or
they hain't time. They don't want to 'ave no
dealin's with blokes like me. Well, I was respect-
able once, mister, but drink plays the devil with a

man. I goes trampin' now, up and down, mister. It hain't so bad in the summer. I was a gentleman once, mister, and once a gentleman, always a gentleman.'

'I believe it.'

He glanced shrewdly at me. 'I'll tell you, mister, there be three rules of the road. I'll give 'em to you, and they may come in 'andy. They be rules what I abides by myself, always 'ave done, for once a gentleman, always a gentleman, I says.'

'What are they?'

'First, make the most of every hopportunity. Second, never go a-begging. Third, always speak the truth.'

'I thank you heartily,' I said. 'They are excellent rules. I will remember them.'

'There's no charge for 'em,' my companion informed me.

'No charge? Thanks,' said I.

'I give 'em to you free, gratis, and for nothink.' He was looking straight before him, perhaps admiring the view.

'I am deeply grateful,' I said.

Then we were silent for a time, each drawing at his pipe, and possibly admiring the view.

After a time the gentleman of the road sighed as if life were a tragedy. 'No,' he said, as if he had been answering a question, 'there hain't no charge for the advice what I've given you.'

'Friend,' said I earnestly, 'I am delighted to hear it.'

So we smoked in silence again, and after a long

time my companion, who was smoking more furiously than I should ever have dreamed of doing, knocked the ashes out of his pipe, examined the bowl critically, and sighed again. I offered him my pouch. 'No thankee,' he replied, 'I'll 'ave a pipeful of twist, I reckon.'

'So you *had* some tobacco?' I challenged.

He nodded. 'Oh yes,' he said. 'But I thought a pipeful of yours would save mine. I never said I 'ad none. I speaks the truth.' He said it rather impudently.

I looked at him curiously, a great, tall fellow, unshaven, uncouth, and yet with a residue of something fine about his face. 'I perceive you speak the truth after a manner,' I said. 'I also see that you do not miss an opportunity. But what about begging a match? How does that fit in with the second of your rules. You begged one from me, you know.'

'What's a match between gentlemen?' he asked.

'Ah well,' I said, 'I see the rules have to be freely interpreted.'

He agreed. 'The fact is, mister, when I was at the top of the 'ill and seed you a-sitting there, I says to myself, I says, "Bill, 'ere's a hopportunity to save a pipeful of baccy an' a match," and I never misses a hopportunity, mister. Never.' He gathered up his long length, pulled his trousers up, lighted his pipe, and grinned. 'It hain't often I 'ave the hopportunity of sittin' an' smokin' a pipe with a gentleman,' he remarked. 'And the advice what I gave you, mister, was hentirely free. No charge whatever!'

'Sir,' said I, also rising to go, 'the pleasure has been mine. Two of your rules I may forget, but one I shall never forget, and will endeavour always to act upon it. I mean, I will always strive never to miss an opportunity of doing good, and I'll begin now.' As I spoke I slipped a fair-sized piece of silver into his ready hand.

He took it with an air of conferring a favour on me by doing so, and as he turned to go I saw the mask slip from his face for a moment. 'Good day to you, mister,' he said, and then, after a pause, 'I reckons I hain't much of a gentleman now, mister, but you don't know the fine feller I once meant to be.'

Those were his last words, for he went down one side of the hill, and I went down the other. It is one chance in a thousand that we shall ever meet again. But I shall not soon forget him. There, but for the grace of God, went I; and though I cut a slightly more important figure in the little circle where I am known, and though a few people regard me as being moderately successful in one particular line, and though I have money enough to keep a roof over my head, and a book or two on my shelves and a vase of flowers on my table, yet I too, if I am humble and honest enough, must say, 'You don't know the man I meant to be.'

By the middle of the afternoon I was in a pleasantly-wooded country where I talked with an old man at a cross-roads, and learned from him that he had four sons, one in India, one in

Canada, one in Australia, and the other in prison. I spoke to a woman in a sun-bonnet, and admired her lupins, whereupon she smiled, and said, 'Oh, flowers always grow well if you treat them kindly.' I went light-heartedly along a good road with roses on the hedge, and silver-fern in the ditch, and a pheasant or two among the corn near by.

Then I came to a turn in the road, and saw a car drawn up at the roadside about two hundred yards farther on. A woman was kneeling by it, so I quickened my pace for I thought I might perhaps be helpful. Few cars, I knew, were likely to come along that road. When I drew nearer I saw the car was jacked up at the rear. The woman had taken one of the wheels off and had been tugging with the spare wheel, but when she saw me hurrying up she stood still, wiping her forehead with the back of her hand. She greeted me with a smile. 'You look like a Good Samaritan,' she said.

'I'm not sure he carried a haversack,' I replied. 'Anyhow, I'll not pass by on the other side. How can I help?'

'It's the stupid jack,' she said. 'It's gone wrong. It will only jack the car half-way up—high enough to get the punctured tyre off, but not high enough for me to get the spare wheel on.'

'Why not let the air out of the tyre?' I suggested, 'and then pump it up again.'

'Brilliant man!' she exclaimed. 'You're perfectly marvellous! I never thought of it. Jim's right. I've all my brains in my boots.'

She looked at her small feet in little shoes, as if to hint that she hadn't any brains at all.

Very attractive she was, diminutive and dark. She moved with a light grace. I judged her to be little more than thirty, and she was certainly extremely pretty. 'We'll soon have things fixed up,' I said. 'I've been in a predicament like this myself.'

I set to work, and she lent a hand—and they were very black little hands, too. She had got the tools all messed up with grease, as I soon found out. 'I'm so annoyed,' she told me. 'I just ran to the Watson's farm—they live a few miles back—and I've only two miles to go, but I simply couldn't drive the wretched thing jolting along like that. Jim will be wondering where in the world I am. He gets so fidgety. A car passed me only a couple of minutes before I had to pull up, and there hasn't been one since. I say, it's awfully good of you to help me like this. And just *look* at your hands! It *is* a shame. I won't half blow them up at the garage about the jack. Don't we look frights? I'm as hot as fire, and all messy, too. I hate it. Never mind, we'll give Jim something to laugh at . . . you'll have to come along with me and get those hands washed, you dirty man!'

'Oh, no, I'll be all right,' I said. It was a lie. 'I'll get them washed somehow.'

'You'll do nothing of the sort. There's not a house till we get to the village, and you aren't fit to be seen. Are you tramping round the country?'

'In a way.'

'What for?'

'Oh, I like it. You get a chance of meeting people in distress, you know.'

She laughed. 'I don't know how many people you've met,' she said. 'I'm a guy. You're a sport. There now, shall I unjack? That's topping. I've had two punctures in a month, isn't it rotten? I'll tell Jim the car's an old crock.'

She helped to pack the tools away, and got into the driver's seat. 'Come along in,' she insisted. 'You needn't think I'm not to be trusted. I'll take you right home, and you can have tea with us—we're plain folk, and have dinner at one, so it will be bread and jam at this time of day!'

I bowed. 'Thanks awfully,' I said, 'but I think if you don't mind . . .' (I was a pilgrim on a *walking* tour, remember.)

'But I mind very much,' she said. 'You were walking this way, so you must be going as far as the village. Get in.'

I got in. 'Men are so stubborn,' she declared. 'They always want their own way.'

'They don't often get it,' I said.

She smiled. 'It isn't good for them,' she admitted. '*We* know best. That's what I tell Jim.' She paused. Then she looked me up and down. 'You must come and cheer Jim up,' she said. 'He'll tell you about himself, perhaps. He is a wonderful man.'

I resigned myself to my fate.

'What are you?' she asked. 'I know it's

frightfully rude, but I've a feeling you are a journalist, or something of that sort.'

I laughed outright. 'Marvellous,' I said. 'Yes, I do indeed belong to the criminal class. How do you do it?'

'I wish I didn't,' she answered, and there was nothing light about her face. 'It's nearly uncanny, isn't it? I often sense things out. It gives Jim the creeps. This time it was easy.'

I didn't ask her why.

Another moment or two and we pulled up outside a little bungalow. It had a charming garden at the front, and a bigger one at the back. There was a veranda on the south side. As we went up the path together she said softly, 'You mustn't be shocked when you see my husband. He's an invalid.' Then she laughed merrily. 'I'll take you in as you are if you don't mind,' she declared. 'You've got a smudge across your literary brow that's priceless.'

So we went into a sunny room, and found a thin man in a wheeled chair. She ran up to him, stretched her hands out behind her, and kissed him. 'Jim,' she said, 'the old crock crocked up finely two miles away, and I got all messed up trying to change the wheel, and the wretched jack wouldn't jack, and this gentleman—he is one, though he doesn't look much of one— came along, and helped me out, and he got all messy doing it, and I made him come to see you and I thought we could spare a bit of soap, what do *you* think?'

He put his head on one side. 'If he'll promise

not to leave it in the water, I dare say we can afford it,' he said.

We laughed. His hand was held out to take mine, but I said a nod would have to do as I wasn't fit to touch him.

She bundled me into the bathroom, and there, with the help of hot water and some scouring powder, I contrived to clean myself. I had not quite shut the door, and just as I was about to come out I caught sight of something in the mirror which made me wince. Apparently this bright little woman had washed her hands more quickly than I, for she had returned to the room, and with the help of another woman, a large, motherly creature whom I judged to be a house-keeper, I saw her lift her husband in the chair, and fasten a strap under his arms and over the back of the chair. I had thought how oddly he was sitting, as if he had slipped. Now he was sitting upright again—but the strap alone kept him in that position. I delayed a little to give them time to get things fixed. Then I went into the room and stood by the window.

I looked down into a bright, laughing pair of eyes, but there were hollow lines under them, and the forehead was wrinkled, and the cheek-bones stood out. We talked about the car, and the weather. I admired the beautiful little house, and praised the garden, and delighted in the view. He chatted pleasantly, and I found that he was—or rather had been—a chartered accoun-tant. He loved books, and we soon found we had many ideas in common. He was an admirer

Nн

of Galsworthy, and so was I. He poked fun at modern free verse, and so did I. We were one on George Meredith, but we differed about Russian literature. I said I wouldn't read it. He said he loved it. As we talked I noticed that he gradually sank in his chair, and presently his wife stood behind him, and, small though she was, lifted him up again and tightened the strap. 'He is such a shocking man,' she said, smiling. 'Instead of hitching his wagon to a star, he tries to go tobogganing under the table. Isn't it ridiculous?'

I said it was.

We had tea, and I learnt that everything was home-made. I praised the cook; and presently I let a remark fall which the bright lady took up, and turning to her husband she told him how she had guessed I was a journalist, and they egged me on till I told them all my adventures, omitting nothing, since they insisted on hearing every detail. They listened with interest. 'And so,' I concluded, 'I met a charming lady who made me come here, and I have found two very brave people here, and when I leave, as I must do shortly, I am going to do an odd thing. I am going to walk through the night.'

'Nonsense,' said the invalid.

'Ridiculous,' said Vi, his wife. 'We haven't a spare bed, but you can have the settee.'

'No,' I said, 'I must do it. I promised myself I would, and I want to. It will be an experience.'

'Well then,' said the managing lady, 'you had better get some sleep before you go on this

wild-goose chase. I'm going down to the village
to blow up the garage. You two men can sit
and talk awhile. Then, when I come back,
you, sir, can go and lie down. We'll keep quiet,
and you can set off at any unearthly hour you
wish—we never go to bed before twelve—Jim
can't sleep.'

I fought against them, but they would have
it so.

Presently, therefore, Jim and I were left alone.
We talked quietly about many things. 'She's a
wonderful woman,' he said at last. 'One in ten
thousand. It nearly breaks my heart that I
should be like this. I've thought sometimes
of finishing myself off—only it would be such
a shock to her. She ought not to be tied to
me in this way—and it may be a year or two
yet.'

I looked at him. I did not know what to say.

'It's creeping paralysis,' he told me. 'There
is nothing to cure it. The doctors have given
me up as hopeless. I know it.' He spoke very
calmly. 'They say it is due to a germ—I don't
know when or how I got it—perhaps in the
trenches, and perhaps not. It has come on
more rapidly this last two years. I was working
till a little over two years ago. Thank God I'm
well insured, and she has a bit of money of her
own. She'll be all right when I've gone.'

I searched my mind for something to say.
He spoke as if it were all so matter-of-fact.
Everything I wanted to say seemed trivial,
senseless; I could not comfort him. It was no

use saying he must not talk in that way, for it was the very best way in which to talk. It was foolish to try to tell him to hope.

He went on talking about himself, almost as if he were someone else discussing the matter. 'What grieves me,' he said, 'is that *she* should suffer so. It hurts her to see me suffer. It makes her a prisoner. She never goes anywhere, never leaves the house except two afternoons a week when she runs over to the farm where we have friends. Even then, she is often back within an hour or so. Look what she misses, and I am a handful, I can tell you . . . would you mind asking Mrs. Richardson to come in a minute?'

The motherly woman came in, and while I wandered out to the veranda, she lifted the invalid in his chair. It was all pathetic, terrible. I wished I had never entered the house.

When I returned he apologized, smiling a rather wan smile. 'So sorry,' he said. 'It's bad for you, too. I sometimes sit and sit, and wonder what it all means. I had such dreams about life, once, and now my little world is growing smaller every day. Strange, isn't it? Well, for a long time I rebelled. I saw no sense or reason in it. I thought God had blundered.'

'You don't think so now?'

'No. I don't think so now. I think we are all in a great family, and I think some of us have to suffer so that others can learn to value health, and ease, and vigour. That's what I think. I told you I'd been an accountant. I think God wanted me to be a preacher. So I've made up my mind to be cheerful to the end—or as near the end as I can. I mean to be brave so that others shall be shamed into using their greater life to more purpose. I can't last very long, and I mean . . .' I saw the hands tremble, lips quiver. The tears stood in his eyes. 'Oh, my God, my God,' he cried as if in agony, 'it means sacrificing everything, everything!'

I stood up. I took his hand in mine, his limp, thin hand, and held it firmly. Then I turned on my heel and went into the garden.

When I went back he was himself again. We talked of war debts and American banking, and presently Vi came back, full of life and freshness and news—the garage man was an idiot, and had apologized; and the Rawlinsons had sold their house at last and were going to live in Buckinghamshire; and the vicar had fallen off his bicycle going round a corner, and had broken a new pair of pince-nez; and the lady at the post office had sent a new book for Jim to see how he liked it. . . .

After a time they bustled me into the next room, and I lay down on the big settee. The heavy curtains were drawn across the window to keep the daylight out, and the house became very still. But I could not sleep. I lay awake, thinking of the two brave people in the bungalow. I thought of all the tragedy under that one roof. I wondered how that little woman kept so bright with so great a fear eating at her heart; how that condemned cripple found strength to face the morrow. I thought that life was infinitely strange and mysterious, deeper than any of us could plumb. Yet however cruel or unjust it might seem, one inevitably found faith and courage and cheerfulness—and even sacrifice.

I think I must have dozed, for I was suddenly aware that eleven o'clock had struck; and feeling guilty of trespassing on the kindness of these brave folk, I showed myself, and asked to be forgiven. Nevertheless, I was the less perturbed, for I had hatched a plot whereby, God willing, I might perhaps bring a little comfort and brightness into their lives; and I am happy to say that already my conspiracy is proving partly successful.

I found the little woman reading to the man. Supper was set, and in a twinkling the kettle was boiling on the electric stove (it had been singing for some time) and coffee was made. They declared that since I was so foolish as to set out at that hour of the night, I must 'fortify' myself, and I had to do justice to the lavish spread in order to please them.

It had struck midnight before they allowed me to go, assuring me that I should be wiser to stay the night, and telling me over and over again that they had been glad to have me, and that they should remember my adventures. They wished me a night without owls or bats, and a safe journey. I felt a pang as I left the house, the little house in the lovely garden, the little house with its great sorrow and its shadow of tragedy, and its two loving hearts beating bravely, come what might. Unknown to them I stood in the road, and, looking back at the lighted window, I prayed to the God of the stars and the secret souls of men to bless and comfort those two.

Then I turned my back on the house and set off along the road.

CHAPTER IX

I walk in the dark; explore a lonely, unfamiliar world; watch the dawn; have breakfast in a little gold mine; hear the involved story of a man with a handcart; ride in company with a remarkable 'bus conductor; am caught in a shower; and walk the last half mile with a shining host.

How LONELY it was! That was my first thought as soon as I had become accustomed to the blue night. There was a young moon low in the west, and there were stars overhead: they seemed very near. I felt I was walking through silence. I went swinging along the road, oddly conscious that the masses of darkness were shimmering in the faint haze of the summer night. They seemed to detach themselves from the hedges and take unexpected shapes. I thought a solitary bush near a gate was a man with his head bowed. I thought an open space which had nothing to catch the faint light was a house; it seemed eerie to find it was only emptiness. I looked over a field of wheat and saw the slow ripples flow towards me as a gentle wind breathed over the sleeping countryside. The road went uphill, and then down into a tunnel under lofty beeches where it was so dark I could not see my hand in front of my face. There was a pale glow at the farther end, and I walked straight on, always keeping my eyes fixed on it. But it trembled, and was deceptive. I thought it was a hundred yards away; it must have been nearly five times as far.

I came to a bridge over a little stream, and saw the stars in the shallow water. There was the smallest elf-like rustle of tiny ripples against the weeds, a low, lapping sound pleasant to hear.

I went on and came to a village with white houses, a grey church amid a desert of tomb-stones, and a pond where I frightened a water rat. Not a door was open, not a window lighted. I felt the loneliness resting on me as a mantle. It seemed to be wrapped round me. The great, sleeping world was inactive at last, but Nature did not sleep. I looked up to see a fluffy thing with large, round, vacant eyes, an owl regarding me with solemn indifference. I heard a little shriek in the hedge—perhaps a ferret had made a successful leap. My ears were sensitive enough to catch the queer cry of a bat fluttering like a lost soul in the vast, blue dome of heaven. I saw it flit across the stars, and in and out of the branches of the trees, feeling its way through a labyrinth of space. The peewits cried in melancholy, restless voices as if disturbed by unhappy dreams. There came sudden little flurries of wind which made sad whisperings in the hedge, and here and there, where there was a sort of passage among the leaves, the wind sighed in a minor key.

The night was alive with sounds, all strange, fascinating. I felt I was walking, not in a familiar world, but in a world I had never known before. The common things of the day were enchanted by night; distances were telescoped, masses quivered, shadows were mysterious, sounds more penetrating and meaningful. A scurry of dust behind me might have been a ghost.

Suddenly I heard a throbbing roar, and stepping back into the hedge I watched a huge searchlight bounding along the road, silhouetting the trees, throwing long, straight beams of shadow across the sky, crowding the smooth road with ribs of light and shade like the wave-marks left on a sandy shore by the ebb-tide. The monster, with its four great eyes, came roaring by, a motor lorry eating up the ribbon of road and clattering through the silence like some infidel desecrating a temple. After it had passed, the night grew closer about me, and shapelessness ruled everywhere for a few minutes. The red tail-light died out, and I was left in a strange, dark world.

I wondered why I had chosen to penetrate it. Should I not have been wiser to have spent the night at the bungalow, or at an inn, with a roof over my head and someone within call? I walked on, and felt I was making acquaintance with a new experience. I felt that I was coming nearer to God in that loneliness than I had ever come before. Humility was in my heart, for the sky was large. I came to a little group of houses. A dog barked in a farmyard. I passed a house with a light in an upper window, and wondered why it was there. Was someone being born into the world? Was someone passing out? It was an odd thought. 'Funny thing, life, isn't it?' That is what the man in the hotel had said. 'A deeply stirring, strangely wonderful thing, life, with its capacity to hold infinite wonder, happiness, suffering, fear, tragedy, unutterable loneliness, and grief.'

I watched the coming of the new day. I saw the first streak of grey in the blue; a long, thin streak in the east, the trees black across it like the bars of a prison. I felt the wind rising, chill, and more chill. I saw the stars pale, and watched the wan light creeping over the fields. I heard a chirping in the hedge. I saw a score of rabbits scamper to their burrows. There was a mist hanging low over marshy land by the river—a thin, white wraith with the light filtering through. The east grew brighter. A narrow line of yellow heralding the rising of the sun lengthened by imperceptible degrees. A few low clouds gathered above it, and presently their lower edges caught a tinge of cadmium. I stood leaning over a five-barred gate to watch the solemn spectacle, to see and feel the earth sink down; but the sun was long in coming. Every minute I thought the growing intensity of the light must burst into fire. The hedges caught the slanting beams, the river shook off its sombre dullness and flamed in midstream, a lark leaped up almost from my feet, its music shaking over me in a cataract of liquid notes. I looked up to follow the singing speck, wondering if it would fall from exhaustion; it seemed the incarnate spirit of praise. I looked up, and by doing so I missed the moment for which I had waited. When I looked down the sun was already half over the tree-clad hills, dazzling, blazing with incandescent splendour, throwing its light like a halo over the wet fields and through the trees, clothing the landscape with sudden light, and long, sleepy shadows. The night was done. Day had returned once more. The earth still slept, but a new day had been given to men, a day without spot or blemish, a new opportunity for service . . . 'I never miss a hopportunity,' the tramp had said. Would to God more of us had his motto in our hearts.

So, greatly daring, I ventured to pilgrim farther in a fresh world. Five miles I walked, and saw not a soul. Then I met a lad on his way to a neighbouring farm. He had a straw in his mouth, and took big strides as he came along the road, his shadow before him. 'Grand morning,' he said.

'Wonderful,' said I.

Miles farther on I saw a farm labourer on a great plough horse, three other horses with him. They came out of a fold-yard, two black, one chestnut, and one white, all beautiful animals. The day's work was beginning for them. 'Morning!' called out the labourer, looking at me in surprise.

'Morning,' said I. We felt we knew each other.

I passed a farm where a woman was letting the chickens out. She nodded to me. I saw a young fellow carrying two buckets of water from a pond. He was whistling 'Annie Laurie.' The world was waking up, and everyone was friendly. 'Sorrow endureth for a night, but joy cometh in the morning.'

It was still barely six o'clock, and I was tired.

I had walked nearly twenty miles, but there seemed little chance of finding anywhere to rest. I determined to press on to the nearest little market-town, for I knew I should be welcome to breakfast there. The thought of two hours' walking appalled me, but I felt I should like to do it, perhaps in order to boast of it afterwards.

I went on. I overtook half a dozen droves of cattle ambling slowly to the market. I came to the town with its single street of shops, its big square overlooked by dreamy old houses and three inns, one of them five hundred years old, another a century older. I passed a colony of red-roofed modern houses, and walked through the shadow of a Norman castle, a shelter for pigeons now that the feudal system has gone. A street from the square brought me to a little shop where newspapers and books and stationery were sold. There was a man at the door watching a boy taking down the shutters. 'Hello,' I said, 'you're late getting the shutters down!'

'Well, I never!' said the man. 'If it isn't enough to astonish anybody! What in the world are *you* doing here at this time of day?'

'Coming in search of breakfast,' said I.

'You've come to the right spot,' said he. 'I can smell mine, and Annie will be delighted to put another rasher of bacon in the pan, and boil a couple more eggs. . . . Bless me, how you do take an old man . . .'

'Fifty-one summers and fifty winters,' I reminded him.

'To be sure—but we live strenuously now.

However, here you are! Come over by 'bus, I expect?'

'No,' I said. 'Walked twenty-seven miles since supper, that's all.'

'Twenty-seven miles? You must be mad!'

'I believe I am. But let me see Annie, and if you happen to have any soap knocking about . . .'

He shook his head sadly. 'You always were a bit of a mystery,' he grumbled. 'Come in, come in. Annie, Annie, just look what's turned up!'

So I was welcomed with a kiss on each cheek, and a reproof at my 'idiotic goings on,' and bustled up to the bathroom. I knew where to find it, and while I washed in hot water, and then splashed in cold, I heard Thomas talking to customers in the shop, and running through to the living-room to tell Annie to make some toast. I chuckled to myself, for I rather thought they would enjoy the thrill of making me welcome. Perhaps it was vanity or presumption to think so, but hadn't I stayed there a score of times, and hadn't they been to stay with me? They were two middle-aged folk who ran a shop with scarcely room to turn round in, but a little gold mine nevertheless, and possibly one of the most satisfactory businesses within fifty miles. A small, droll man was Tom Shaw, whose wife was anything but diminutive, but you might travel a long way without finding two people who understood each other better, or got more out of life. You might wonder what they could get out of life, the man in his shop most of the day, the woman doing much of the housework, and both tucked away in a little market-town. But they undoubtedly *did* get a good deal out of it.

I went down to breakfast, and was compelled to give an account of myself, which I did dutifully, though Tom heard little more than half of it, for he kept running into the shop to serve customers, and there were more than you might have expected. But patience achieves all things, and within the hour I had not only told them most of my adventures, but had learnt how things were going with them. Annie was busy 'getting-up' a garden party in someone else's garden, the proceeds to go towards re-pewing the church. The arrangements took up a good deal of her spare time, for, of course, she was bound to attend the clinic one afternoon a week, and she had her 'old ladies' to look after, dear souls whom she had somehow taken under her wing, and made a practice of visiting every so often. 'Poor, dear Mrs. Hutchinson has died since you were here,' she said, 'and her last words were, "God bless you, my dear." It was worth all the bit of trouble to have that.'

It transpired, moreover, that Tom was pushing a new line in local guides—he showed me one, and I promptly bought it. He had also been using his spare time (these people talked of spare time as if there were no end to it) in taking photographs of the church, inside and out, and making postcards of them. They were going well, and would go better when the tourist season got into full swing. He had had a lot of trouble with the County Council owing to the new water-scheme on hand, and nasty things had been said about him, but his conscience was clear, and he had acted as he had thought best. As chairman of a local Antiquarian Society he had read two papers in the preceding session, one on the heraldry of the fifteenth century as it appertained to the immediate neighbourhood; and one on the last siege, and the subsequent demolition, of the castle, a subject to which his attention had been drawn by the publication of certain family papers of the seventeenth century. He was happy to say that he had increased his commission on the advertisements for which he was the local agent; and, smiling as he told me, he had handled another five matrimonial affairs which he believed to be shaping favourably.

'So,' said Annie, 'we have not been idle since you saw us last.'

'You seem to have been doing a little,' I said.

Annie looked at me severely. 'As for you,' she said, 'you ought to have more sense at your time of life than to go wandering about the countryside at night. The best thing you can do is to go straight up to bed and sleep till the middle of the afternoon.'

'No, gracious madam,' said I, mocking her, for we are great friends; 'I fear I must not do so, though I do not doubt the wisdom of it. Have I ever known you to be wrong? But I intend finishing my travels to-day, and I am thinking of taking a 'bus from this town to within a few miles of home.' (I had not stressed the fact that I was, more or less, on a walking tour.)

'Why not ride all the way?' Tom rapped out.

'Because,' said I, 'I think it will be pleasant to walk into my own town. It is a foolish fancy . . .'

He took me up, quoting Tom Hood: 'But now 'tis little joy, to know I'm farther off from heaven, than when I was a boy.'

I was left in peace for an hour. I dozed and read the morning paper in the tiny garden at the back of the house, a garden with a mulberry tree 300 years old, and a peep of the grey castle above the red roofs of the upstart houses. Annie came out to sit with me awhile, talking quietly, and unconsciously revealing all her wonderful plans for helping people; and telling me, half in secret, that sometimes she really had to restrain Tom because there was never a tramp came into the shop, but what Tom gave him something to help him on his journey, and, as she had often pointed out, there was reason in all things, and one *had* to draw the line somewhere.

I agreed heartily.

Presently Tom ran in to say he had told the shop-girl not to call him for half an hour—unless it was a matrimonial affair, because he had just remembered a little story he was sure I should be delighted to hear, and might even care to put into my book. 'I meant to write and tell you about it,' he explained, 'but what with one thing and another—and Annie . . .'

'Very well, sir,' said she rising with great and offended dignity, 'I will go.'

So she went. He looked after her, and waved

Oн

his hand. Then he took off his spectacles and polished them thoughtfully. 'Wonderful woman,' he said. 'Heart of gold, patience of Job, simplicity of a child. Her affections run away with her sometimes, you know. I have to remonstrate now and then. She heard of a woman being down and out, and made broth for her, and gave her a new dress and a pair of shoes. Dash it all, you know, we're not millionaires, one ought to draw the line somewhere.'

I agreed heartily. 'But the story?' I asked.

'Ah, yes. Well, you may not think much of it, but I thought it beautiful. I know everyone hereabouts, or nearly. Well, one cold, wet night in March, the oddest thing happened. I'm not sure I can remember all the details, it was so horribly complicated. I ought to have written it down for you at the time. Anyhow, I didn't. Well, it was about the biggest mix-up you could imagine, and the queer thing was the way it threw light on one or two folk hereabouts, and showed me something about them I hadn't known. As for the dear boy, he died last month, but that's neither here nor there. What I was going to say was that I was coming back from taking the chair at the Institute about a quarter to ten one night, and was just turning into the High Street when I heard voices.

'There was a policeman with a notebook in his hand, a representative of the law who had only just come to the town. There was also a little man. He wore a thin overcoat, and an old cap, and as I came up I noticed that he kept flinging out his hands. "Yes, but hold on a minute," he was saying, "just a minute. You might let a chap explain. You see, well, if you wouldn't be so hard on a chap, and just let him explain. After all, it's no distance, and the passage is just over there."

' "I want your name," said the policeman. He was evidently bent on doing his duty.

'The little man seemed desperate. "Yes, but hold on a minute," he said again. "Don't be hard on a fellow. Everybody here knows me."

'The policeman said he didn't, and he added that he wanted no nonsense, and that he must have the little man's name at once. "It's no good you starting all over again," he said. "There isn't a light on this handcart, and if you want to make a speech about it, you will have an opportunity when you come before the magistrates."

'I remember how the little man pulled off his cap and was continually screwing it up in his hands. He was just in the middle of a defence of himself when he caught sight of me. "Hi, mister," he shouted, "he's caught me right enough, but it does seem a shame with the passage only a yard or two away. You see," he went on, "this business hasn't anything to do with me, not really. It's George's idea—you know, George Robson—and he has been going to do it for months, only something's always stopped him, and of course the boy had been looking forward to it for weeks."

' "What boy?" the policeman inquired.

' "Teddy Greenwood," the little man replied

eagerly. "You'll know him, mister; he's been ill for months."

'I told him I knew him very well, and after a glance at what was on the handcart, I added, "Am I right in thinking that you took your gramophone round this evening?"

'He shook his head, and said it wasn't his gramophone, and that he couldn't afford one. He explained that it belonged to Brown, the coal merchant, and pointed to the passage close by.

'The policeman looked at me, and then, with a little less severity, he said, "So you were taking Mr. Brown's gramophone back on your handcart?"

' "Yes, that's it," the little man said breathlessly, "I'm taking the gramophone back, only it isn't my handcart."

'That complicated matters a good deal, and I remember how the policeman pushed his hat back and scratched his head as if he could make nothing of it all.

'The little man took advantage of our bewilderment. "Things *do* seem a bit mixed up, don't they?" he asked. "That's why I wanted to explain. You see, we couldn't find the lamp anywhere."

'The mention of the lamp reminded the policeman of his duty. He asked to be informed who the parties were that couldn't find the lamp, and the man with the handcart made another attempt to explain. "It's this way," he told us. "It was Robson who wanted to give Teddy

Greenwood a pleasant evening, so he borrowed Brown's gramophone, and arranged with Mr. Priestley to lend him his handcart so's he could take the gramophone up to Teddy Greenwood's. Well, Mr. Priestley left the handcart in his yard, but he forgot to leave the lamp on it, and he has had to go away to see a friend of his who is in trouble, though I don't know what's the matter with him; and his wife, I mean Mrs. Priestley, didn't know where the lamp was, and she said he was too careless for anything, and we hunted high and low, and couldn't find it."

'This was the policeman's opportunity, and he made the most of it, impressing on the little man the fact that if the lamp couldn't be found it was his duty to have postponed the musical evening. I remember how the culprit threw out his hands again as if quite exasperated. "Yes, yes, I know," he confessed, "but you see, the boy had been looking forward to this evening for ages, and he had been disappointed once before, and Robson said he hadn't the heart to disappoint him again."

'It struck me as being odd that Robson had not taken the gramophone himself. I asked why. My query brought another torrent of explanations.

' "There you are," said the little man, "that's another reason why I wanted to explain. It's all a terrible mix up. You see, there is an old woman lives next door to them, I mean next door to the Robsons, and she's a poor, lonely old soul, and Mr. Robson was going this evening, only this afternoon the old woman knocked at the wall, and Mrs. Robson ran into her house, and found her on the floor. She had had a stroke, or something. Well, there wasn't nobody to look after her, and the doctor said she hadn't to be left, and they've wired for her married daughter, but she can't get here till to-morrow; and Mr. Robson's little girl is in bed with measles, though she's getting over them now, and he couldn't get a neighbour in to look after her, so of course he could not go, and he wasn't very well, either. Then I just happened to call round at his house, and he said that I should have to put the show on for him. So I went round to Mr. Priestley's to borrow the handcart, and then went to Brown's and got the gramophone and records, and then went up to Teddy Greenwood's, and we had a grand time, I can tell you. It made me cry to watch that lad when the music was on. It was just wonderful. He seemed to forget everything, and we put every blessed record on twice. And you see, I wouldn't have come back with the gramophone to-night, seeing as how I didn't get a lamp, only Priestley said Robson was to be sure and let him have the handcart because he wanted it first thing in the morning."

'By this time the little man's cap was screwed up so tightly that I thought it would never again be fit to wear. Even the constable seemed impressed by his amazing narrative of events, and when I suggested to him that the rain seemed to have blown over, and that the stars were shining again, he took the hint, and told the little man that he was never to let him catch him with a handcart without a light again.'

'You are right,' said I, 'it *is* an odd story. It makes you feel there is more kindness in the world than we are sometimes inclined to believe. If you don't mind, I'll make a note or two about it, the actual names don't matter, and I think I'll put it into an account of my adventures. By the way, I suppose you didn't send anything to the poor boy? No grapes, or books, anything of that sort? One has to draw the line somewhere, you know.'

He chuckled. His chuckle is one of the drollest things about this droll man. 'I'll be getting back to business now,' he said. 'You stay and rest awhile.'

I acted on his advice, and two hours later I was still sitting out there in the garden. I had lost most of my tiredness, and was beginning to feel ready for the last stretch of the journey.

We had dinner at one, and they talked so much—these two people who really had no idea whatever where to draw the line—that it was after four o'clock before I was thoroughly out of the shop, and even then Tom must needs come walking down the street with me to see me safely in the 'bus. 'Friend of mine, the conductor,' he said. Then, glancing at the man in question, he remarked, 'Look after him for me, Stanley.'

'Right you are,' said Stanley. 'I'll do my best. This side up, perishable. So long!'

I sat down at the rear of the 'bus, and the conductor sat by me. 'Funny old boy,' he remarked, jerking his thumb at the roundish figure waving his hand to me. 'Did me a good turn once, though. I shan't forget it in a hurry.' He talked pleasantly till we were a mile or so out of the town. Then he stood up, and staggered down the 'bus, punching tickets. I held out a ten-shilling note. 'Sorry I've nothing less,' I said.

He selected a pink ticket and punched it before replying rather whimsically, 'You needn't be sorry. In fact, you ought to be glad!'

'You mean that it is better to have ten shillings than ten pence?'

'There are two ways of being rich,' he replied, when he had counted out my change. 'One is to have all you want, the other is to be satisfied with what you've got!'

There was something ingenuous about him in spite of his shrewd glance.

'Men and women may be divided into two classes—those who see a 'bus conductor, and those who don't!' he said after a pause. 'I mean, some people who travel by 'bus hold out their fare and look through the window as if the conductor were nothing. They pocket their change without even a "thank you." On the slightest pretext they lodge a complaint against his number. I pity them!'

'You are actually sorry for them?'

He nodded. 'Once I was angry with them. I lost two posts through what the companies were pleased to call incivility to the passengers. God knows all I did was to tell them the truth. After all, sir, a 'bus conductor is a man, flesh and blood. He may be working to support a wife and children, but there is nothing wrong in that—it should make him worthy of courtesy and consideration. I used to get angry with the snobs, but now . . .' He shrugged his shoulders. 'I can't afford to. I merely study the passengers, and place them, so to speak, in one or other of my two classes of mankind, those who don't see me, and those who do. The first, as I say, I'm sorry for; the second I'm glad of. They thank me for giving them change, and apologize because they have nothing less than a ten-shilling note.' (Here his eyes kindled mischievously.) 'They give even a 'bus conductor his self-respect, and make life worth living—and ticket-punching a useful service. They save a chap from becoming a cynic, shorten the dreary journey, and when at last they step out of the 'bus they leave a pleasant feeling behind.'

He became suddenly self-conscious, and though he talked a good part of the way, he did not choose to show me any more of his secret thoughts.

In an hour and a half I covered more miles than I had tramped in all my night march. It was good to be travelling nearer my home. That was something. I was glad when we picked up a young fellow who was evidently a friend of the philosophical 'bus conductor, for my thoughts were all the company I needed. My pilgrimage had been worth while. Nevertheless, it was good to be going home. I suppose I ought to have grown out of sentimental thoughts about my own garden, the creaking gate, and the dog which would be waiting to bound towards me, his tail a-quiver with a loyal greeting. I have not.

We pulled up at a half-way house. The 'bus would have taken me on another five miles to my own town, but I had no mind to finish a *walking* tour in a 'bus, so I said 'Good-bye' to the conductor, and went into the inn where I ordered strawberries and cream, brown bread and butter, and a pot of tea. When I had finished the meal and paid my reckoning, I lighted my pipe, and shouldered my haversack. Then I bought a bar of chocolate for a little boy who was sitting on a doorstep. He had looked up at me, and asked, 'Do you like my trousers? My Mum made them for me.'

Glancing up at the sky, heavy with clouds, I set off for home.

There was no need to hurry, and I was content to tramp along at an easy pace. I wondered what my friends would say to me when my arrival was noised abroad. I went down hill and then up hill. I passed a gipsy camp, and saw the blue smoke rising from a wood fire in a quarry. I came to a cottage where I knew I should be sure to find a welcome, but I did not knock at the door. I kept right on. I thought of Thomas à Kempis whom I had neglected somewhat, and pulling him out of my pocket I sought for a few comfortable words. I found them at the end of the third book, and read them aloud as I plodded on in the warm glow of the evening:

'Bless and sanctify my soul with Thy heavenly blessings, that it may become Thy holy habitation, and the seat of Thine eternal glory; and let nothing be found in this temple of Thy dignity which shall offend the eyes of Thy majesty.

'According to the greatness of Thy goodness and the multitude of Thy mercies look upon me, and hear the prayer of Thy poor servant. Protect and keep the soul of me, the meanest of Thy servants, amidst the many dangers of this corruptible life; and by Thy grace accompanying direct me along the way of peace to the land of the everlasting light. Amen.'

They were beautiful words, and they sank like music into my soul. They cheered me on. I heard eight o'clock strike in the tower of the last church I had to pass before seeing my own town. I knew every turn of the road. Another mile, and I should look down on a well-loved scene. But the clouds were gathering, and there was a wind in my face. The sun was hidden, and soon the rain came down. I confess that my spirits sank. This was not quite how I had pictured my last mile. I took shelter under a friendly tree. The rain came down hard, slanting against the narrow bit of landscape I could see, streaking like light across a grey world. For twenty minutes I was a prisoner. Then the shower ceased as quickly as it had begun. The sky cleared, and the sun burst through the clouds again for a brief triumph. Leaving my shelter, I walked into the radiance of the sparkling countryside from which the scent of flowers and grass rose like incense. Every leaf was spangled with pearls, the brilliant reflection of the sky shone on the common road. There was gold in the pools, and music in the gutters.

I turned a corner where the hedges fell back, and saw the town, its western windows ablaze with crimson, its towers and spires rising up in majesty above the dazzling roofs. It had been wonderful to leave home. It was more wonderful to come back. Gladly I went down the hill; and when I had gone a little way I looked behind me. The wet road was afire with golden splendour: *I was walking along a shining highway.*

It seemed to me as if, in that majestic moment, I renewed my fellowship with all I had met during my pilgrimage . . . the disgruntled young man who had a gracious spirit; the humorist who drove a gig and told laughable stories; the man who found that it wasn't all bread and dripping being a Christian; dignified Christopher walking arm-in-arm with his lady. I caught again the sound of voices singing in the little Methodist chapel, heard the preacher bidding us go into all the world and live the gospel, saw the old man in the choir, his face radiant. Down the hill came the tramp with shreds of gentlemanhood about him; the hero of the bungalow walking with manly steps; the landlord of *The Three Wise Men*, his pipe sending a wreath of smoke against the setting sun. I remembered Charlie with his bunch of wild flowers; the parson who might have written a best-seller had he been a lesser man; the young enthusiast who had said, 'Life isn't easy, thank heaven.' I saw Mr. Quinn pushing Mr. Washington in a Bath chair; the boy who had all the world before him, and loved birds, and stars, and things; the 'bus conductor who had a philosophy of his own; my friend, the newsagent, who didn't know where to draw the line; the lady who mended socks; George who loved 'hosses'; the youth who hated boots and potatoes . . . all these, and many more, were my companions. They were the common, every-day saints and heroes whose little lives and triumphs, whose sacrifices and services go un-recorded except by that good Spirit which sees and knows all the ways of men. How proud I was to go down the hill in company with this splendid host.

And now the country was left behind. The sun was down and the shining highway was a common road again. I turned two corners, and saw my own home, the door wide open. I pushed the gate. It had the old, familiar creak.

Printed *in* Great Britain
By The Camelot Press Ltd
London *and* Southampton